BEASTARS

Volume 10

Story & Art by

Paru Itagaki

STORY & CAST OF CHARACTERS

Plot Treatment...

Cherryton Academy is an integrated boarding school for a diverse group of carnivores and herbivores. Recently Tem, an alpaca member of the Drama Club, was slain and devoured on campus. Since then tensions between predators and prey have been running high...

Just when it seems like Tem's murder will remain unsolved, gray wolf Legoshi deduces that the perpetrator is a fellow member of the Drama Club, brown bear Riz. Now Riz wants to kill Legoshi, as well as Dall bighorn sheep Pina, who accidentally saw Legoshi accuse Riz.

Legoshi continues to train at the black market to prepare for a grand reckoning with Riz. One day, he runs into red deer Louis. Legoshi is bewildered to see his herbivore friend leading the Shishi-gumi lion gang. Louis has changed so much, yet Legoshi's tail automatically wags with joy at seeing his friend again. As the two speak, Legoshi realizes Louis is a moon shining in the darkness, a beast living with dignity in the depraved black market. Legoshi departs with a lump in his throat.

Cherryton Academy announces that starting next term, carnivores and herbivores will be assigned to separate classes. Many students protest the ruling. Meanwhile, Riz mentally relives his relationship with Tem, including its tragic end...

Things are coming to a head!

BEASTARS

Legoshi

★Gray wolf ♂
★High school second-year
★Member of the Drama Club production crew
★Physically powerful yet emotionally sensitive
★Struggles with his identity as a carnivore

Louis

★Red deer ♂
★High school third-year
★Former leader of the Drama Club actors pool, but now leader of the Shishi-gumi

Haru

★Netherland dwarf rabbit ♀
★High school third-year
★Member of the Gardening Club

Juno

★Gray wolf ♀
★High school first-year
★Member of the Drama Club actors pool

Gohin

★Giant panda ♂
★Psychologist who runs a clinic at the black market

Riz

★Brown bear ♂
★High school second-y
★Member of the Drama Club sound crew

Pina

★Dall bighorn sheep ♂
★High school first-year
★Member of the Drama Club actors pool

BEASTARS
Volume 10

CONTENTS

80
Picking and Choosing Smiles.....8

81
Eyes like Two Side-by-Side Pieces of Lacquerware.....31

82
Across the Universe.....51

83
An Ordinary Hug Handled by a Futon.....71

84
Turbulent Air Swirling Around Those Hands.....92

85
Will Our Blood Not Flow Together Even in the Sewer?.....115

86
A Comet in the Depths.....135

87
Best Supporting Actor Award for the New Star.....155

88
An Intense Woman.....175

The story...
...is about to begin.

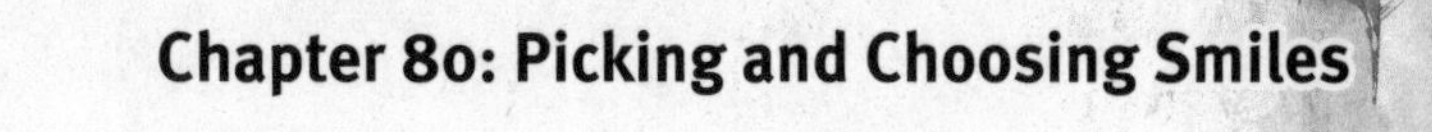

Chapter 80: Picking and Choosing Smiles

BEASTARS
Vol. 10

WOULD YOU TASTE GOOD IF I ATE YOU?

IS THAT GALLOWS HUMOR YOU SHARE WITH OTHER HERBI- VORES?
TEE HEE. WAS IT FUNNY?

IF I WERE A CARNIVORE, I THINK YOU'D LOOK TASTY... HERE, FOR EXAMPLE...
TEE HEE! I CAN'T IMAGINE YOU AS A CARNIVORE.
...
WHY NOT?
OUR PAWS ARE SO SLENDER AND SMALL...
I BET BOTH OF US TASTE GOOD.

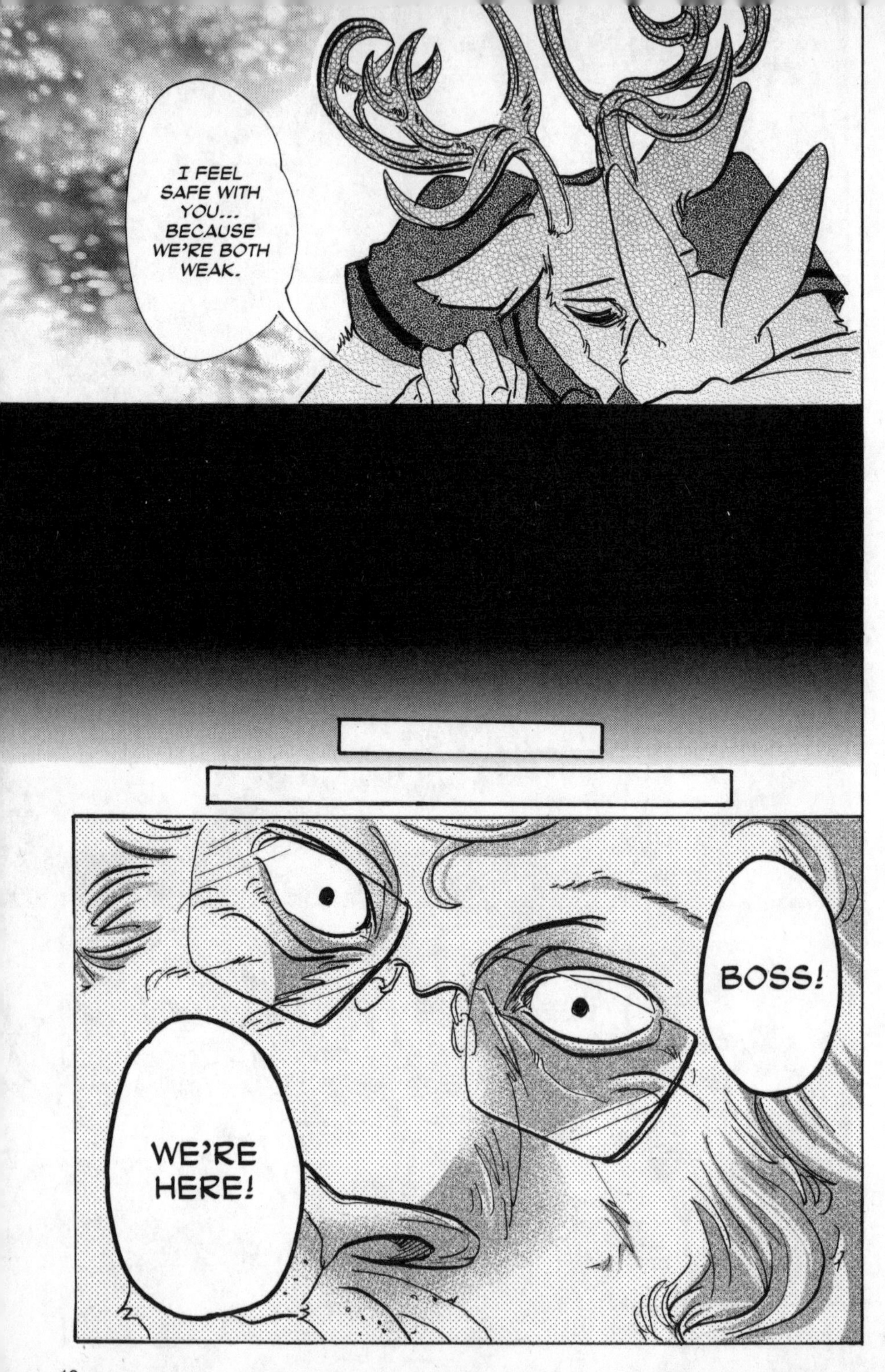
I FEEL SAFE WITH YOU... BECAUSE WE'RE BOTH WEAK.
BOSS!
WE'RE HERE!

SORRY TO WAKE YOU.
I apologize.
...
NO PROBLEM.
I HAVEN'T DREAMED ABOUT HARU FOR THE LONGEST TIME... WHY NOW?
GREETINGS, SHISHIGUMI!
I DON'T FEEL A THING ANYMORE WHEN I SEE HERBIVORE MEAT BEING SOLD IN THE BLACK MARKET.

IT'S BEEN FOUR MONTHS SINCE I STARTED WORKING WITH THESE LIONS...
I'VE LEARNED A LOT OF NEW THINGS.
Carnivore Drugs
LIKE THE FACT THAT CARNI-VORES AREN'T THE ONLY ONES WHO COME TO THE BLACK MARKET TO EAT MEAT...
THERE ARE NO RULES HERE.
HUF HUF
HUF
HUF
I DISCOV-ERED THAT WHEN...

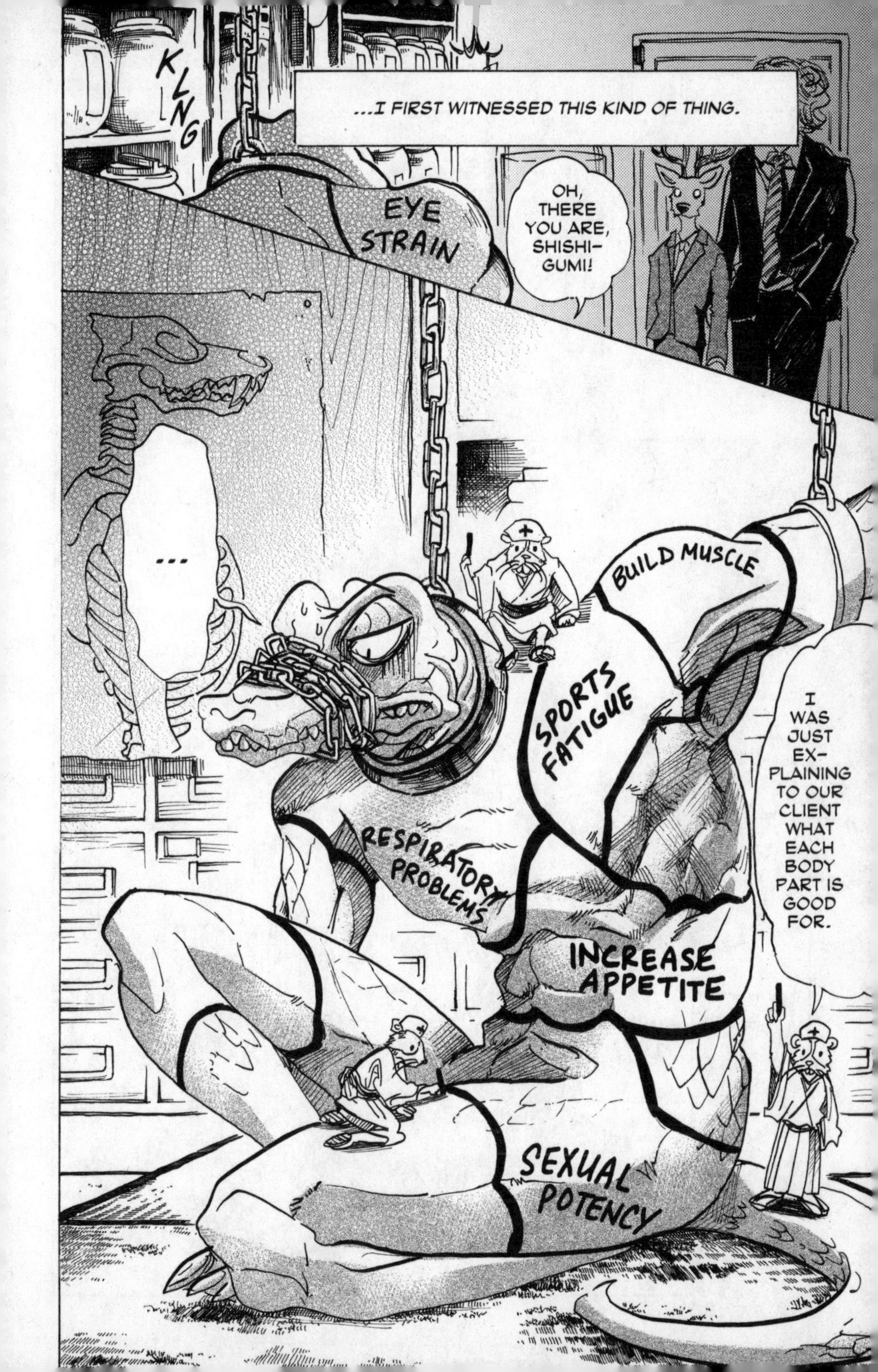
KLNG
...I FIRST WITNESSED THIS KIND OF THING.
OH, THERE YOU ARE, SHISHI-GUMI!
EYE STRAIN
...
BUILD MUSCLE
SPORTS FATIGUE
I WAS JUST EX-PLAINING TO OUR CLIENT WHAT EACH BODY PART IS GOOD FOR.
RESPIRATORY PROBLEMS
INCREASE APPETITE
SEXUAL POTENCY

BURIED DEEP INSIDE THE BLACK MARKET IS A TRADE IN CARNIVORE FLESH.
HE'S AN OLD GOAT.
The customer
I GUESS HE'S RESIGNED TO HIS FATE NOW.
HEY, WE RUSHED OVER BECAUSE YOU TOLD US YOUR "INGREDIENT" WAS GETTING AGITATED. BUT HE LOOKS PRETTY QUIET TO ME.
HE DECIDED TO SELL HIMSELF. NO ONE FORCED HIM TO.
MISTER GOAT, YOU'RE LUCKY. CAIMAN* FLESH IS VERY RARE.
*A subspecies of crocodile

ARE YOU SURE THIS WILL...
...CURE MY CHRONIC ILLNESS?
OF COURSE!
CARNIVORE DRUGS WORK WONDERS!
THEIR SALES PITCH ALWAYS SOUNDS PHONY.
UH-HUH. (I TOTALLY AGREE.) BUT DON'T INTERFERE WITH THEIR BUSINESS.
CARNIVORE DRUGS...
MEDICATIONS COMPOUNDED FROM A MIXTURE OF CRUDE DRUGS AND CARNIVORE INGREDIENTS.

Welfare
THIS QUACKERY WAS INVENTED BECAUSE HERBIVORES CRAVE POWER.
WEALTHY HERBIVORES DESPERATE TO CURE THEIR FAILING HEALTH WILL TRY ANY TREATMENT.
EYE STRAIN

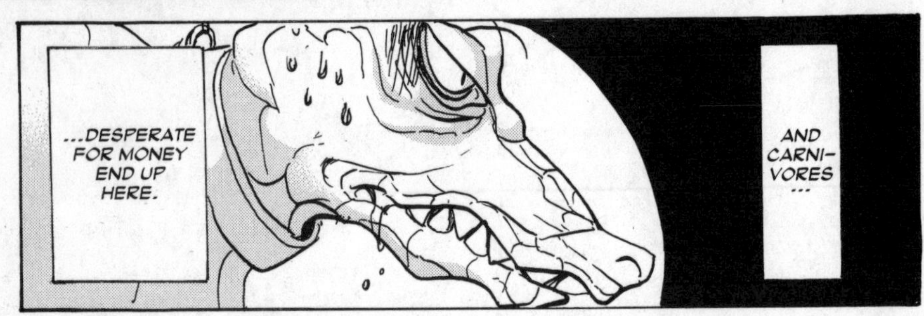
AND CARNIVORES...
...DESPERATE FOR MONEY END UP HERE.

I'M D-DOING THIS FOR THE CASH...
SO PLEASE REMOVE A PART THAT WON'T KILL ME...
BUILD MUSCLE
SPORTS FATIGUE

YES, YES...
FOOD-STUFF! HOW OLD ARE YOU...?
Ahahaha...
I'M 37. I HAD TO BORROW MONEY FROM A LOAN SHARK, AND I CAN'T REPAY IT...
THE RELATIONSHIP BETWEEN CARNIVORES AND HERBIVORES IS INVERTED HERE.

I SEE. YOU'RE YOUNG.
MY LOWER BODY HAS BEEN PARALYZED FOR TEN YEARS.
KREEK
KREEK
KREEK
I WANT TO HAVE SEX WITH MY WIFE JUST ONCE BEFORE I DIE... FOR THE SAKE OF OUR MARRIAGE...
SO PLEASE, DOCTOR...
Sochiku
EYE STRAIN
SURE. PREPARE TO SEVER HIS SEXUAL ORGAN, ALL RIGHT?
SNAP
YEP!
H-HEY...
...WAIT! WHAT DID YOU JUST SAY?! AREN'T YOU GOING TO USE ANES-THETI—?

ARRRRGH! AHHHHHH!
SHF
IBUKI?
HEY!
HOW COME YOU'RE ACTING LIKE A DAD ALL OF A SUDDEN?!
CUT IT OUT!

YOU'RE ONLY 18, BOSS.
YOU SHOULDN'T SEE THINGS YOU DON'T NEED TO.
ISN'T IT KIND OF LATE FOR THAT, IBUKI? AND YOU'RE ALREADY AN ADULT AT 18.
THAT WAS A SIGHT WE HAVEN'T SEEN OUR-SELVES IN A WHILE THOUGH...
They cut off his penis...
I'LL BET HE'S MAD.
SORRY, BOSS...

CARNIVORE DRUGS BRING IN A LOT OF REVENUE.
I'M TAKING FULL ADVANTAGE OF MY STATUS AS AN HERBIVORE TO PROTECT THIS BUSINESS.
ALL THE DOCTORS ARE NERVOUS GUINEA PIGS. THEY AGREED TO HIRE US AS THEIR MUSCLE THE SECOND THEY LAID EYES ON ME— A DEER.
YEP! IT'S ALL THANKS TO YOU, BOSS!
We're real grateful.

I ♥ THE BLACK MARKET
Udon Noodles
I...

THINGS WERE A LOT HARSHER FOR ME GROWING UP THAN YOU CAN IMAGINE.
I WASN'T RAISED LIKE YOU LIONS. YOU HAD HAPPY CHILD-HOODS.

GO AHEAD AND GO BACK TO YOUR CARS. I'M GOING TO HAVE A SMOKE.
O-OKAY.
...
UM...
IBUKI REALLY MAKES A FUSS OVER THE BOSS.
HE BECAME HIS PER-SONAL AIDE BEFORE WE KNEW IT.

I'M INDEPENDENT NOW.
ONCE, I WAS JUST A FAWN ON SALE HERE TO BE DEVOURED ALIVE...
BUT NOW I'M THE ONE IN CONTROL OF THE BLACK MARKET.

EVERYONE ELSE IS WEAK. THEY ALL BOW DOWN TO SOCIETY'S RULES.
BOSS!
DON'T JUMP TO YOUR DEATH!
WHY WOULD I WANT TO KILL MY-SELF?
BECAUSE... I JUST FIGURED OUT... WHAT YOUR BACKGROUND IS FROM WHAT YOU JUST TOLD US.
IT'S A BEAUTIFUL NIGHT, ISN'T IT...?

ENERGY

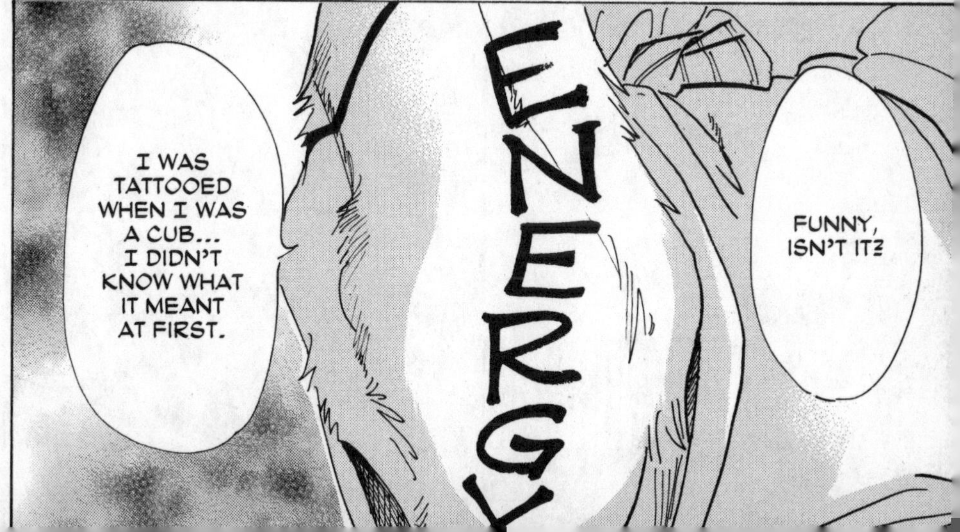
FUNNY, ISN'T IT?
I WAS TATTOOED WHEN I WAS A CUB... I DIDN'T KNOW WHAT IT MEANT AT FIRST.
ENERGY

I RAN AWAY. I WAS ALL ON MY OWN. BUT I MANAGED TO RAISE MYSELF UP.
WE'RE ALIKE, YOU AND ME.
...
BIIIP BIIIP
BIIIP
BIIIP BIIIP
BIIIP
Haru
I SHOULD HAVE REAL-IZED IT ALL ALONG.
BUT NOW I CAN FEEL IT IN MY BONES.

IT'S A SIN TO LIVE YOUR LIFE AS AN ORDINARY, WEAK BEAST.
IT'S COLD TO-NIGHT, IBUKI.
WANT TO JOIN ME FOR A DRINK?
I'LL DRINK WITH YOU UNTIL THE SUN COMES OUT!

MMM...
SLURP SLURP
THE DOCTORS TOLD ME MILK WILL HELP ME HEAL FASTER!
I'M GLAD I HAVE A LONG TONGUE. IT COMES IN USEFUL AT A TIME LIKE THIS.
MY ARM GOT STITCHED BACK ON, BUT I NEED TO WORK HARD AT MY PHYSICAL THERAPY IF I WANT IT TO MOVE LIKE BEFORE.
HEY!

Chapter 81: Eyes like Two Side-by-Side Pieces of Lacquerware

I CAN'T TALK TO YOU IF YOU'RE SO FAR AWAY, TAO!

KIBI...
I... I SHOULDN'T HAVE COME TO SEE YOU... I'M SORRY... THESE FLOWERS...

COME OVER HERE.
COME COME
...
I'M FINE...
TODAY'S A WEEK-DAY. DID YOU CUT CLASSES?
I DON'T HAVE CLASSES TODAY... I MEAN...
I'VE BEEN SUSPENDED FOR TWO WEEKS. I DESERVE TO BE PUNISHED, OF COURSE.
YOU CAN'T BRUSH THIS OFF AS A FREAK ACCIDENT.
WE WERE JUST STRETCHING TOGETHER... AND THEN... THAT TERRIBLE THING HAPPENED...

EVEN IF I TOLD YOU I DIDN'T DO IT ON PURPOSE...
...IT WOULDN'T MEAN ANYTHING.
I DON'T KNOW HOW TO APOLOGIZE TO YOU!
TAO...
WILL YOU TOUCH MY RIGHT PAW?
WHAT?
W-WHAT ARE YOU SAYING...? HOW CAN I TOUCH YOU?!
I RIPPED YOUR ARM OFF!
IT'S ALL RIGHT!

I'VE DECIDED NOT TO TOUCH HERBI-VORES ANYMORE !!
BUT YOU CAME TO SEE ME!
I DON'T WANT TO STAY SCARED OF CARNIVORES.
I WANT YOU TO TOUCH ME AGAIN BECAUSE I WANT US TO MAKE UP.
Just... be gentle...

SQWEEN
!!
YOUR FINGERS MOVED! DOES THAT MEAN YOUR NERVES HAVE RE-CONNECTED?!
HEH HEH... I ONLY JUST RECOVERED SOME SEN-SATION THIS MORNING.
YEAH! I'LL BE FINE AFTER I FINISH MY REHABILI-TATION!
R- REALLY? YOU MEAN... THERE'S HOPE?

I GOT HURT... BUT YOU GOT HURT TOO, TAO.
I'M SO GLAD YOU CAME TO SEE ME.
KIBI'S ARM IS GETTING BETTER!
om: Tao
To: Domu
Hi.
I went to see Kibi yesterday.
He's recovered some sensation in his right arm, and it looks like he'll be able to move it like before after physical therapy.
KIBI COULDN'T MOVE HIS ARM YET WHEN YOU VISITED HIM, RIGHT?! THIS IS SUCH GOOD NEWS!
Yeah...
LOOKS LIKE KIBI'S EFFORT IS PAYING OFF.

MAYBE I'LL GO VISIT HIM TOO...
LOOM
RIZ...
YEAH! HE'D BE HAPPY TO SEE YOU!
"MAYBE I'LL GO VISIT HIM TOO"?! WHAT THE HELL?!
HE'S THE ONLY CLUB MEMBER WHO CAN'T CONTROL HIS IN-STINCTS...
I HAVE TO PROTECT EVERY-ONE...
HE DEVOURED A FELLOW CLUB MEMBER...
LEGOSHI! THIS LIGHT, IT— HUH?

LEGOSHI... DID YOU JUST... GROWL?
ARE YOU MAD?
I DON'T WANT TO TELL ANYONE UNTIL I'VE COME TO TERMS WITH IT MYSELF.
SORRY! IT WAS JUST A HICCUP.
TAO GOT SUSPENDED FOR TWO WEEKS. WAS THAT THE ONLY OPTION THE SCHOOL HAD?
IT WAS APPROPRIATE.
TAKE IT EASY... HAVE TO KEEP CALM... CALM...
TAO DIDN'T DO IT ON PURPOSE, BUT HE STILL HURT KIBI.
HE COMMITTED A GRAVE SIN BY FAILING TO BE CONSIDERATE OF HIS FELLOW HERBIVORES.
WHAT?
twitch
twitch

NNGH!
KRUSH
KRUSH
KRUSH

TWITCH
YOU DEVOURED AN HERBIVORE! WHAT RIGHT DO YOU HAVE TO SAY THAT?!
ARE YOU MORALIZING TO YOURSELF?
TELL ME, RIZ...
L-Legoshi?!

ENOUGH.
EVERYONE'S WATCHING.
I DON'T CARE... BUT YOU DO, DON'T YOU?

HOW GRAVE IS TAO'S SIN?!
STOP, LEGOSHI!
WHAT THE HELL IS GOING ON?!
SHEESH... WOULD SOMEBODY STOP THEM?!
CARNIVORES NEED TO CONTROL THEIR EMOTIONS.
SO I'M BETTER THAN YOU.
I'M NOT SUFFERING ANYMORE, PSYCHOLOGICALLY.
BECAUSE I KNOW WHAT MY HERBIVORE FRIEND TASTES LIKE...
GASP

AGH!
OWW OWW...
HOW
COULD
YOU?

I'M SPEAKING ON BEHALF OF THIS EQUIPMENT, OF COURSE!
SHEESH... PULL YOURSELF TOGETHER, LEGOSHI!

PI... NA...
YOU HAVE TO QUIT DESTROYING THINGS...
RIGHT, RIZ?
I-I'M SORRY...
YES, AND ...?
AND I'LL PAY FOR THE EQUIPMENT I BROKE...
ALL RIGHT. YOU'VE MADE RESTITUTION.
PROBLEM SOLVED.
HMPH. COME ON, LET'S REHEARSE, EVERYONE!
Pina
A- ALL RIGHT!
IS EVERYONE HERE?
...

...
THIS MONSTER IS OVERTHINKING THINGS AGAIN...
SIGH
STOP FORCING ME TO CLEAN UP AFTER YOU, WILL YOU? WE'RE THE ONLY ONES WHO KNOW THAT RIZ KILLED AND DEVOURED TEM.
Don't you know how to act cool?
I'M SORRY, I'M SORRY, I'M SORRY... I REALLY AM...
I GET WHY YOU'RE SO MAD THOUGH. RIZ IS GOOD AT ACTING THE PART OF THE NICE BEAR.
HE'S THE COMPLETE OPPOSITE OF YOU.

I HAVE YOU AS AN ALLY... BUT RIZ MUST FEEL SO ALONE BECAUSE HE'S HIDING HIS CRIME.
I'D NEVER BE ABLE TO STICK IT OUT... HOW DOES HE STAY SO CALM?
TODAY, I FELT THE PRESENCE OF AN IMPENETRABLE WALL BETWEEN US...
LIKE THE ONE THAT SEPARATES VIRGINS AND NON-VIRGINS?
Y-YEAH... SOMETHING LIKE THAT!

EVERYONE VIEWS THE WORLD DIFFERENTLY, DEPENDING ON WHETHER THEY'VE EXPERIENCED SOMETHING OR NOT.
MAYBE I SHOULD TRY TO UNDERSTAND HIS PERSPECTIVE...
NO NO NO!
WHAT THE HELL?! WHY WOULD YOU WANT TO MEET A CRIMINAL HALFWAY?!
Scolding him like a senior classmate
ANYONE HAS THE POTENTIAL TO BECOME A CRIMINAL...
...ESPECIALLY A CARNIVORE.
LEGOSHI... ARE YOU SAYING YOU WANT TO DEVOUR ME...
...TO RELATE TO RIZ BETTER?

NO! NOT AT ALL!
BUT I THINK I'VE FINALLY FIGURED OUT HOW TO RESOLVE THIS.
I NEED TO FIGHT HIM WITH MY FISTS SO WE CAN TRULY UNDERSTAND EACH OTHER!
AND I MIGHT BE ABLE TO DO THAT... I HAVE TO HURRY THOUGH!
See you!
SHEESH... AT THIS RATE, I WOULDN'T BE SURPRISED TO SEE LEGOSHI ON THE LATE-NIGHT NEWS TOMORROW...
Not my problem though.

Chapter 82: Across the Universe

WERE LARVAE ALWAYS THIS SMALL?
EVEN THOUGH IT'S TINY, IT'S MOVING... IT HAS A WILL OF ITS OWN...
BUT I ALREADY KNEW THAT.

Chapter 82: Across the Universe

TALK TO ME, INSECTS.
KASHAK
I'VE BEEN FASCINATED BY INSECTS SINCE I WAS A PUP...
I NEED YOUR HELP.

AREN'T YOU GOING TO COOK THEM FIRST OR SOMETHING?

NO.
I'LL EAT THEM... ALIVE.

WEIRD RITUALS IN MY WORKPLACE... *THAT'S* A SURPRISE.
WHAT THE HELL ARE THOSE CANDLES FOR?
UM...
I THOUGHT THEIR SOULS MIGHT FIND IT EASIER TO DIE IN PEACE IF THERE WERE FLAMES NEARBY.
The insects' souls, I mean...
I took my shirt off to be more connected to nature...
UM... BUT NOW I'M GETTING NERVOUS.
GOHIN... HAVE YOU EVER EATEN INSECTS?
NOPE. PANDAS HAVE NO INTEREST IN CONSUMING LIVE PROTEIN.
MEALS WITH INSECT PARTS ARE LEGAL... IF THEY'RE USED FOR SOUP STOCK OR AS FLOURS. I KNOW THEY'RE HIGHLY PRIZED BY CARNIVORES.
Rhinoceros beetle protein
Ant shake
PURE DRIN
Cricket tea
HOWEVER...

BEASTS STILL AVOID EATING INSECTS IF THEY LOOK LIKE INSECTS.
NO ONE WANTS TO TAKE A LIFE.

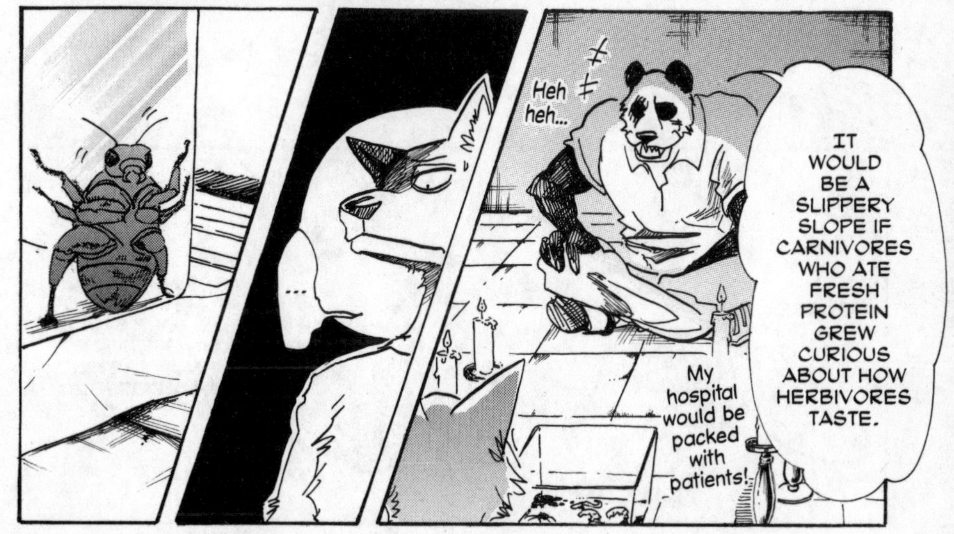
...
Heh heh...
IT WOULD BE A SLIPPERY SLOPE IF CARNIVORES WHO ATE FRESH PROTEIN GREW CURIOUS ABOUT HOW HERBIVORES TASTE.
My hospital would be packed with patients!

THE SIN...
...OF EATING LIFE...
I PUT OFF EATING THESE INSECTS UNTIL NOW.
I WASN'T GOING TO EAT THEM TODAY IF YOU STOPPED ME.

WHO AM I TO THINK I'M SUPERIOR TO THEM ...?
THIS LARVA IS TRYING ITS BEST TO SURVIVE...
WHAT GIVES ME THE RIGHT TO EAT IT JUST BECAUSE IT'S AN INSECT?
WHY DO I THINK I'M BETTER THAN IT...?
WHAT THE HELL ?!

YOU'RE JUST REALIZING THIS NOW?! YOU ALWAYS THINK YOU'RE BETTER THAN EVERYBODY ELSE.
NO ...
YOU'RE A VIRGIN... YOU BEAT THE CRAP OUT OF MALES YOU DISAPPROVE OF... YOU JUDGE EVERYONE... YOU'VE BEEN CHASING AFTER THE SAME RABBIT FOREVER...
I SOUND PATHETIC ...
YOUR LONGING TO PROTECT OTHER BEASTS INCREASES YOUR NATURAL CARNIVORE AGGRESSIVE-NESS...
NAH, IT'S OKAY...

RIGHT... I ONLY WANT TO BECOME MORE LIKE... RIZ THE BROWN BEAR...
...SO I CAN CRUSH HIM... WITH MY BARE PAWS!

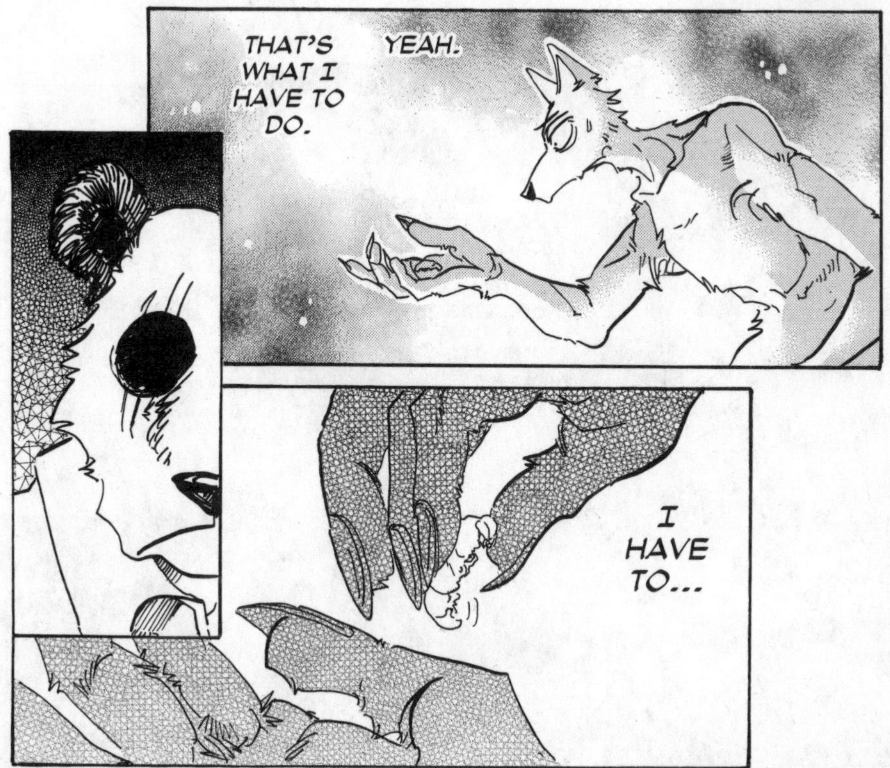
YEAH.
THAT'S WHAT I HAVE TO DO.
I HAVE TO...

FORGIVE...
...ME.
TEACH ME...
...ABOUT LIFE.
I'M GOING TO EAT YOU NOW...
CHMP

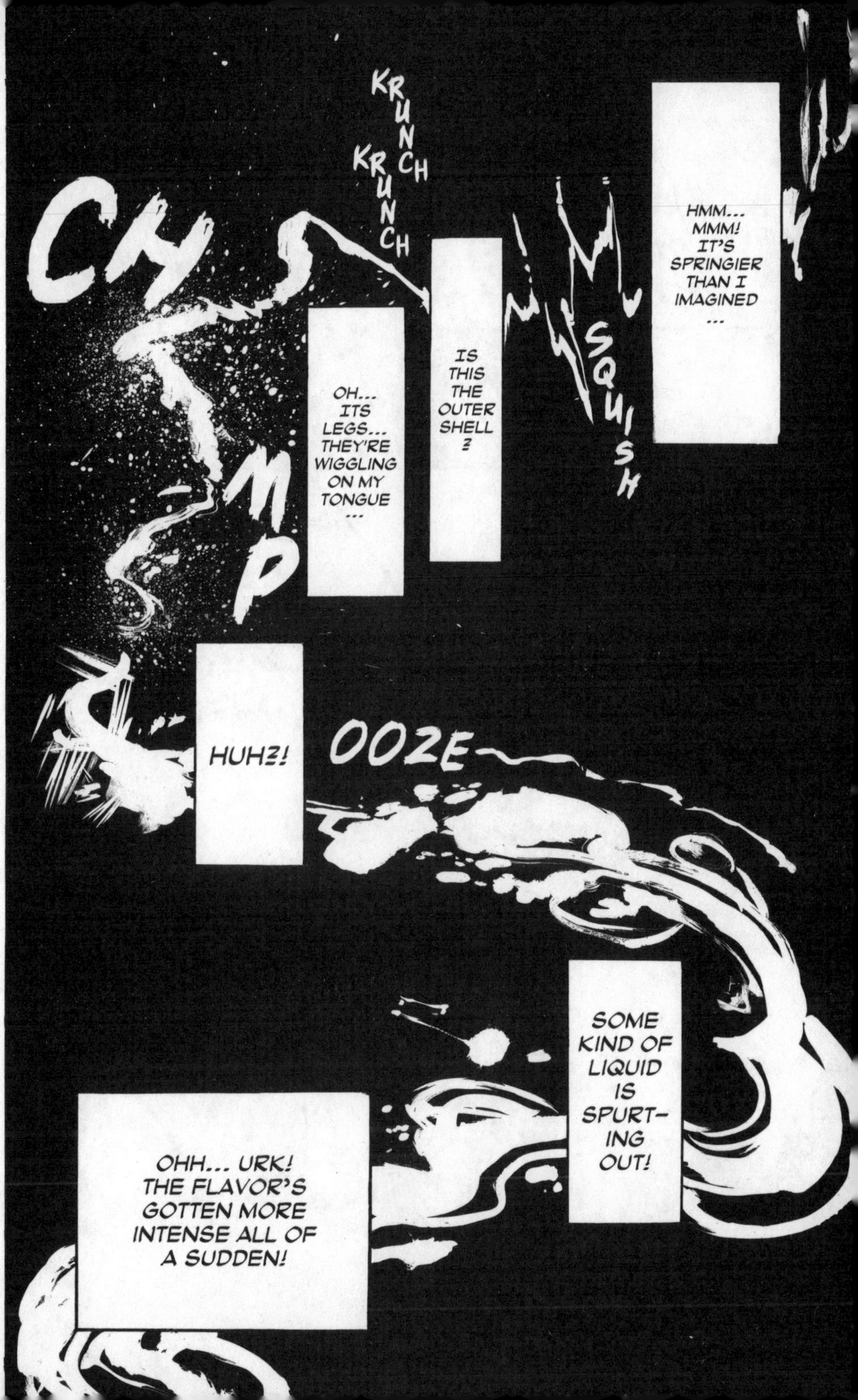

HMM... MMM! IT'S SPRINGIER THAN I IMAGINED ...

SQUISH

IS THIS THE OUTER SHELL?

KRUNCH KRUNCH

OH... ITS LEGS... THEY'RE WIGGLING ON MY TONGUE ...

CHOMP

HUH?!

OOZE

SOME KIND OF LIQUID IS SPURT-ING OUT!

OHH... URK! THE FLAVOR'S GOTTEN MORE INTENSE ALL OF A SUDDEN!

I TASTE BITTERNESS...
...AND SALTINESS...
I CAN SMELL GRASS...
...THE EARTH... AND WIND...
THIS FLAVOR IS SO RICH...
...AND COMPLEX...
THIS FLAVOR IS FULL OF MEANING...
SO THIS...
...IS THE TASTE OF LIFE!
MMFF!
WAIT!

ARE YOU GOING TO SPIT ME OUT...
...YOUNG ONE?
A...
...MOTH?!
BECAUSE OF YOU, I'LL NEVER BE ABLE TO DEVELOP INTO THIS FORM...

GULP
I'M ...
... SORRY.
MOTH... I... I SAW YOU MOVING ON MY PALM. BUT...
...I PUT YOU IN MY MOUTH ANYWAY.
I DIDN'T VALUE... YOUR LIFE.
I THOUGHT IT WAS ALL RIGHT TO EAT YOU BECAUSE I WANTED TO GET STRONGER. I DISCRIMINATED AGAINST YOU, A LIVING BEING...
PLEASE REBUKE ME! I'LL ACCEPT ANY PUNISHMENT YOU CHOOSE. I KNOW WHAT I DID IS UNFORGIVABLE.

DE-VALUING LIFE...
DISCRIMINATION...
PUNISHMENT...
FORGIVENESS...
THOSE WORDS ARE MEANINGLESS TO US INSECTS...
OUR CONSCIOUSNESS IS SOLELY DEVOTED TO LIVING.

WE HAVE NO LANGUAGE OR EARTHLY DESIRES.
WE LIVE IN AN INFINITELY SIMPLE AND HONEST WORLD.
THE ONLY THING WE VALUE...
...IS RESPECT FOR LIFE...
RESPECT... FOR LIFE...
I WISH ...

...I'D BEEN BORN AN INSECT INSTEAD OF A WOLF.
I CAN SPEAK. I HAVE AMBITIONS. LIFE IS HARD FOR ME BECAUSE I'M FULL OF THOUGHTS.
...
SNIFF
AN INSECT'S LIFE ISN'T EASY EITHER, YOU KNOW.
I GUESS NOT...
I'm sorry.
I'M GLAD I SPENT THIS TIME WITH YOU. NOW I CAN REST IN PEACE.
IT'S TIME TO SAY GOODBYE, POWERFUL ONE.
MAKE ME YOUR FLESH AND BLOOD...
...AND FOLLOW YOUR DESTINY.

LIFE IS BEAUTI- FUL.
HEY... YOU'RE AWAKE!
H- HOW...
...LONG WAS I OUT ...?
ABOUT TEN MINUTES.
YOU COL- LAPSED JUST AFTER YOU CLOSED YOUR EYES AND ATE THAT LARVA.
WELL? ARE YOU HOOKED ON FRESH PROTEIN NOW?!
BWAHAHAHA
NO. THIS IS THE LAST TIME I'M EVER GOING TO EAT ANY.
IT WAS JUST A BITE, YET I FEEL SO TIRED... I CAN BARELY LIFT A FINGER...
QUIT WHINING. TAKE A LOOK AT YOUR- SELF IN A MIRROR LATER.

YOU LOOK PRETTY GOOD NOW!
Oh... My fur...

Chapter 83: An Ordinary Hug Handled by a Futon

HEY, LEGOSHI!
HOW DID YOUR FUR GROW BACK SO QUICKLY? I CAN SEE YOUR FACIAL MARKINGS AGAIN TOO...
WHAT ...?
BECAUSE I DRANK A LOT OF SEAWEED SOUP, I GUESS.
Really?
I'VE NEVER SEEN YOU DRINK ANY...

OWW! CAREFUL WITH THOSE HORNS!
SORRY!
MORNIN'.
MORNIN'.

MY FUR GREW BACK REALLY FAST AFTER I ATE THAT LARVA TWO DAYS AGO.
THE NAPE OF MY NECK FEELS SAFE NOW THAT IT'S COVERED IN FUR AGAIN. IT'S BEEN A WHILE...
SWISH

WE HAVE NO LANGUAGE OR EARTHLY DESIRES.
WE LIVE IN AN INFINITELY SIMPLE AND HONEST WORLD.

I HAD SOME KIND OF VISION OR DREAM...
BUT I STILL FEEL LIKE THAT MOTH TOLD ME SOME-THING PRO-FOUND.

NEVERTHELESS...

...I'M A...

...JUST HAD A SEXY DREAM ABOUT HARU...

I'M POWERLESS OVER MY PRIMAL URGES! I'M JUST AN ORDINARY YOUNG MALE NO MATTER WHAT I DO!
WHICH MEANS I'M STILL FULL OF EARTHLY DESIRES! I'M A BAG OF EARTHLY DESIRES! I ATE AN INSECT, AND MY FUR GREW! THAT WAS ALL!
THIS ISN'T THE FIRST TIME I'VE HAD A HOT DREAM ABOUT HARU EITHER...
SHE'S APPEARED IN MY DREAMS IN ALL KINDS OF SITUATIONS... BUT WHY? WHAT PART OF MY UNCONSCIOUS IS GENERATING THESE SCENES?
THEY'RE AWFULLY REALISTIC TOO... I FEEL LIKE I'M ACTUALLY TOUCHING AND SMELLING HER!
KLNCH KLNCH
HER PAWS ARE SO SOFT— UNLIKE ANY PART OF MY BODY...

HEY!
YOU'RE GETTING HANDSY, LEGOSHI...
SQWEEZ
SQWEEZ
SQWEEZ
SQ WEEZ
!!! YOU'RE REAL!
REAL...? HUH?
I'M SORRY!
I DON'T MIND, THOUGH.
H-HARU! WHAT ARE YOU DOING IN MY CLASS-ROOM...?
WHY ARE YOU HERE?
YOU TOLD ME YOU'RE IN CLASS C. I THOUGHT I'D DROP BY.
YOUR CLASSES ARE OVER FOR THE DAY, RIGHT?
I WANTED TO SEE YOU...
...AND TALK TO YOU.
ARE YOU FREE?

WE HAVEN'T HAD A GOOD, LONG TALK SINCE YOU PROPOSED TO ME THAT DAY...
...

I PREFER NOT TO TALK HERE THOUGH. LET'S GO SOME-WHERE ELSE.
ALL RIGHT. I HAVE SOME TIME BEFORE I HAVE TO HEAD OVER TO DRAMA CLUB. LET'S TALK.
LEGOSHI SEEMS TO...
...HAVE MADE SOME KIND OF RESOLUTION OR SOMETHING...
THAT CHAIR'S HIGH— BE CAREFUL GETTING DOWN.
HE'S BEING SO NICE TO ME...
C'MON, LET'S GO.

Cleanup Week
HOW ARE YOUR CLASSES GOING, HARU?
MEH... THEY'RE ALL RIGHT.
IT'S FUNNY HOW HE ACTS LIKE MY DAD SOMETIMES.
LOUIS WAS THE COMPLETE OPPOSITE. HE ACTED LIKE A FAWN.
HE WAS MENTALLY UNSTABLE BUT PRETENDED TO BE STRONG... HE WAS MEAN...
AND HE ALWAYS SEEMED LONELY.

IT'S A BEAUTIFUL DAY OUT TODAY...

LEGOSHI... I LIKE YOU.
I REALLY LIKE YOU.
WHAT ?!
WHAT ...?
HUH? REALLY ?

THIS IS... THE FIRST TIME SHE'S TOLD ME THAT... I THINK.
YOU'RE STRONG... NICE... HUGE... I CAN DEPEND ON YOU.
THANK YOU.
THE MORE I LIKE YOU, THE MORE I WORRY ABOUT LOUIS.

URK! THAT CAME OUT WRONG! D-DON'T MISUNDERSTAND ME!
IT'S NOT THAT I STILL HAVE FEELINGS FOR HIM!
...
LEGOSHI, LISTEN TO ME!
LOUIS AND I USED TO BE LOVERS...
...BUT THAT'S ALL OVER NOW. I'M NOT IN LOVE WITH HIM ANYMORE.
BUT I DO STILL WORRY ABOUT HIM... I CALLED HIM THE OTHER DAY...
HE PICKED UP, BUT THEN HE HUNG UP.
THE WAY HERBIVORES FEEL ABOUT BEING OUT OF TOUCH... IT'S DIFFERENT FROM THE WAY IT IS BETWEEN HERBIVORES AND CARNIVORES.
I'M WORRIED HE MIGHT BE IN DANGER...

SHEESH...
LOUIS IS SUCH AN IDIOT.
I FEEL SO POWER-LESS...
ALL A WEAK BEAST LIKE ME CAN DO IS WORRY ABOUT OTHER BEASTS...
...EVEN IF THEY'RE CLOSE FRIENDS.
HOW CAN I BE THINKING INAPPRO-PRIATE THOUGHTS AT A TIME LIKE THIS?
ALL I WANT TO DO IS...
...HUG HER...

BUT IN MY DREAMS, I...
...HOLD YOU AS TIGHTLY AS I CAN...
...AND... HAVE MY WAY WITH YOU...
"YOU CAN KEEP CHARGING TOWARDS THE LIGHT!"
"BE A HERO!"
I'M NO HERO.
MY LUST ALWAYS GETS THE BETTER OF ME.
I'M JUST A HORNY MALE TEENAGER.

HARU... YOU'RE SO SMALL.
SNIFF... HUH?!
THE SIZE OF MY BODY DEFINES MY EXISTENCE.
EVERY-THING ABOUT ME HAS CHANGED...
...SINCE THE DAY I FIRST MET... AND ATTACKED... YOU.
YOUR SCENT, YOUR TINY FRAME... YOU DON'T NEED TO CHANGE A THING ABOUT YOU.
ARGH!
I JUST WANT YOU TO FEEL SAFE.
GRAB

I'LL TAKE CARE OF EVERY-THING!

I WON'T LET ANY BEASTS SUFFER!
LEGO... SHI?
Self-control
...
NNGH

I HAVE TO ACT NOW, DO WHAT IT TAKES...
...TO BRING LOUIS BACK TO SCHOOL.

MY EARTHLY DESIRES GIVE ME STRENGTH!
I'LL TAKE CARE OF HIM FOR YOU, HARU. AND THEN I'LL HOLD YOU TIGHT.

YOU ALWAYS HAVE A HANKIE ON YOU...
SNIFF
Sorry, I need to go to Drama Club now. Do you want to wipe your tears with this?
You can keep it...

Boys' Locker Room

SHEDDING SEASON'S FINALLY OVER...
I LOST A TON OF FUR LAST MONTH!
WAS THE FLOOR OF YOUR DORM ROOM COV-ERED WITH HAIR?
IT WAS LIKE I HAD A FUR RUG.
YIKES!
Boys' Locker Room
I WON'T LET ANY BEAST SUFFER ...
KA-CHAK

IT'S JUST THE TWO OF US HERE NOW.
NOT EVEN YOU.
RIZ...

...young one...
Go on...

Chapter 84: Turbulent Air Swirling Around Those Hands

BEASTARS
Vol. 10

JUST THE TWO OF US...
...IN THIS REALLY SMALL ROOM...
Wild Kick

AREN'T YOU SCARED...
...LEGO-SHI?

I'M NOT SCARED.
I'M CURIOUS... ABOUT HOW YOU MANAGE TO KEEP UP APPEAR-ANCES.

DON'T YOU DARE CALL ME BY NAME WHILE LOOKING AT ME LIKE A PREDATOR!
YOU MAKE ME SICK.
THIS GRAY WOLF...
...IS DIFFERENT FROM OTHER CARNIVORES.

YOU UNDER-STAND ME TOO WELL.
I'VE NEVER SEEN SUCH A... DELICIOUS-LOOKING BODY.
I WANT TO BOND WITH YOU... NOT BY TALKING TO YOU, BUT BY DEVOUR-ING YOU...
...LEGOSHI.
TUP

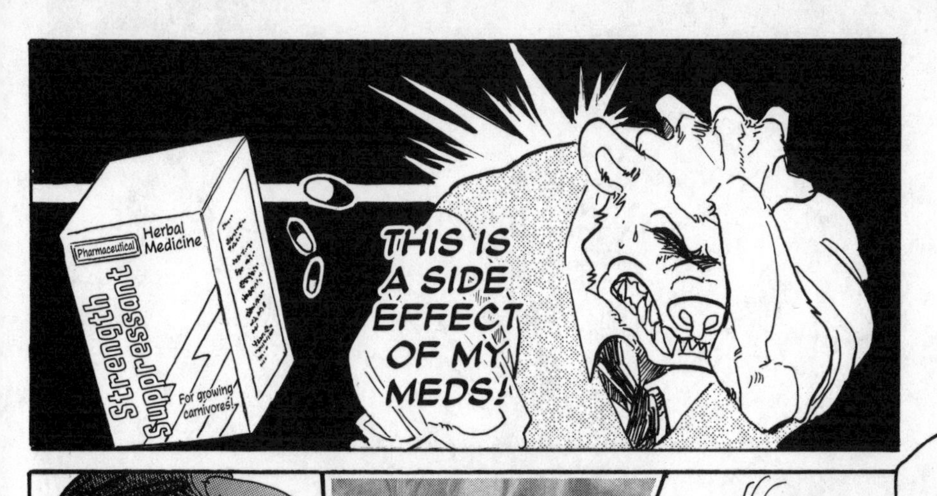
Pharmaceutical
Herbal Medicine
Strength Suppressant
For growing carnivores!
THIS IS A SIDE EFFECT OF MY MEDS!

WHERE'S MY HONEY ...?
I HAVE TO SUPPRESS THIS...
I CAN'T STAND THIS HEAD-ACHE!
SUNFLOWER
HONEY

BAM
HONEY
I'M DOING PHYSICAL TRAINING UNDER THE SUPERVISION OF A MEDICAL DOCTOR NOW.
I UNDERSTAND WHAT URSIDAE GO THROUGH.
THUNK
FLOWER
YOU'RE FORCED TO TAKE MEDI-CATIONS. THAT MUST SUCK.
I'M USED TO BEING FORCED TO DO THINGS. I DON'T MIND THAT.
DAMN IT... THESE SIDE EFFECTS...
MY HEAD... DAMN...

HUF HUF
HUF HUF
I FEEL ...
...LIKE MY HEAD'S GOING TO SPLIT IN TWO...
DO YOU HAVE ANY IDEA...
...HOW I SUFFER FROM THE SIDE EFFECTS OF THESE STRENGTH-SUPPRESSING MEDS? THE STRESS I GO THROUGH?

THERE. THAT'S BETTER. I PREFER THAT YOU LOOK AT ME LIKE THIS.
SHOW ME ALL THE SAVAGERY INSIDE YOU.
...
HUF HUF
I'M GOING TO CRUSH YOU AND AVENGE TEM!
LEGOSHI...
WE CARNIVORES HAVE SUCH TINY PUPILS, DON'T WE?
WHAT HAVE WE SEEN WITH THEM...
...FOR THE LAST 17 YEARS?

THE MORE CLOSELY I'VE LOOKED...
...THE MORE I'VE REALIZED THE ONLY THING INSIDE ME IS SOLITUDE.

I THINK YOU MIGHT BE ABLE TO UNDER-STAND...

...MY SOLITUDE.
TUP
TNGL
NGH...

driiip
HIS PAWS ARE HUGE...

WILL THIS BLOOD HAMPER MY FIGHTING ?
YEAH.
I CAN'T SEE TOO WELL...
BAM

Boys' Locker Room
NNGH... URRGH...
I BET THAT HURTS. BUT YOU CAN TAKE IT. HERE, THIS WILL STANCH YOUR BLEEDING.
GAH! ARGH...
I'LL MAKE SURE NO ONE INTERRUPTS US.
WE WON'T LEAVE A TRACE.
MY MEAL WILL BE SACRED!

I'LL TAKE YOU SOME-WHERE...
...NO ONE WILL SEE US.
WHERE'S LEGOSHI AND RIZ?
DUNNO. I SAW THEM IN THE LOCKER ROOM.
WE CAN BLEED AS MUCH AS WE WANT HERE.

WE CAN WASH AWAY OUR BLOOD...
...AND THIS SHOWER ROOM IS STURDY.
ONCE WE CARNIVORES EAT A BEAST ALIVE, WE START SELF-HARMING... OUT OF GUILT AND HUNGER...
WOW, OUR HIGH SCHOOL YEARS REALLY SUCK...

I'LL REGAIN MY LOST YOUTH BY DEVOUR-ING YOU!

GO AHEAD. ENJOY BEING A TEEN-AGER.
RRIP
BUT I'M GOING TO RIP OPEN YOUR OLD WOUNDS...

THEY'RE NOT OLD WOUNDS!
THEY'RE PRECIOUS MEMORIES!
I BONDED WITH TEM!
WE CAN ONLY OVERCOME THE DIVIDE BETWEEN THE SPECIES BY DEVOURING OTHER BEASTS!

ONLY
LOVE...

...CAN OVERCOME THE DIVIDE BETWEEN THE SPECIES!
THAT'S... TRUE!
WHY DIDN'T I...
...RE-ALIZE IT BE-FORE?
WHAT YOU WANTED TO TEACH ME...
AND HOW GEN-TLE YOU WERE...
...GRAND-PA.

YOU LOOK JUST LIKE YOUR OLD GRANDPA, LEGOSHI! COME ON, LET'S PLAY!

Chapter 85:
Will Our Blood Not Flow Together Even in the Sewer?
This Komodo dragon always appeared whenever there was an interspecies conflict.
Gosha (when he was 17)
Every species feared him because he was incredibly big and powerful.
But one day on the battlefield, he fell in love with a female wolf... and was never seen again.

IS THAT RUMOR TRUE?
Legoshi, 12 years old
ARE YOU REALLY A DAN-GEROUS LIZARD?
WHAT?
HEH HEH... LEGOSHI... DID YOUR MALE CLASSMATES SAY SOMETHING AGAIN? I HOPE THEY AREN'T BULLYING YOU.
HUP
NO, THEY'RE NOT.

DO YOU HATE YOURSELF BECAUSE A QUARTER OF YOUR BLOOD IS REPTILIAN?
That's sad.
NO, I DON'T.

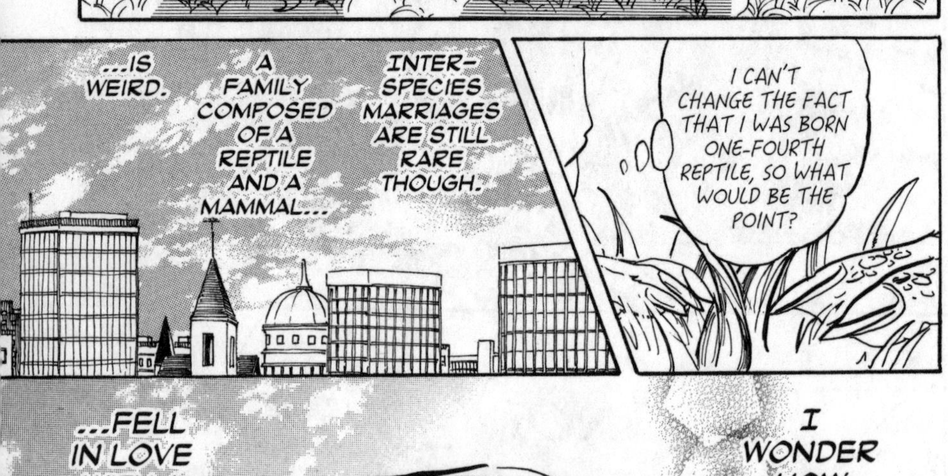
I CAN'T CHANGE THE FACT THAT I WAS BORN ONE-FOURTH REPTILE, SO WHAT WOULD BE THE POINT?
INTER-SPECIES MARRIAGES ARE STILL RARE THOUGH.
A FAMILY COMPOSED OF A REPTILE AND A MAMMAL...
...IS WEIRD.

I WONDER HOW GRANDPA...
...FELL IN LOVE WITH A WOLF...

THAT WAS A BEAUTIFUL FUNERAL SERVICE.
LEGOSHI ... FROM NOW ON...
... YOU'LL LIVE WITH ME.
NO!
HOW CAN YOU BE SO HAPPY?
YOUR DAUGHTER SUFFERED SO MUCH... DON'T YOU CARE ABOUT HER AT ALL?

MOM COMMIT-TED SUICIDE BECAUSE ...
......
I'M SORRY, GRANDPA.

THE FLOOR BROKE. LET ME HIT YOU INSTEAD.
HAVE TO CONCEN-TRATE... HAVE TO CONCEN-TRATE...

HE'S INJURED TOO... BUT HIS PUNCH CARRIES A LOT MORE WEIGHT THAN MINE.
THROB
THROB
B-BBMP
B-BBMP
I WILL NOT...
...DIE HERE!
Nngh
CHMP
HA HA HA...
ARE YOU TRYING TO DEFEND YOURSELF?

GO AHEAD AND TRY CHEW-ING WOLF MEAT...
IF YOU DO, YOU'LL NEVER BE ABLE TO USE YOUR JAWS AGAIN!
CHMP
♪ LA LA LAAA...

HMPH.
THE BOYS' SHOWER ROOM IS AWFULLY DIRTY TODAY.
IT'S AN HERBIVORE.
SNIFF
The cleaning lady...
EH?
UM... IS SOMEONE INSIDE?
OR IS IT JUST MY IMAGINATION? I'M COMING IN!
DAMN! WHAT ARE YOU GOING TO DO, RIZ?!

EXCUSE ME, MISS!
I'M SORRY, I'M STILL USING THE SHOWER.
WHAT? YOU'RE NOT SUPPOSED TO BE SHOWERING NOW.
I'M SORRY, I LOST TRACK OF THE TIME. COULD YOU HOLD ON FOR FIVE MINUTES?

WELL, ALL RIGHT.
I'VE GOT A JOB TO DO, SO MAKE SURE YOU'RE OUT IN FIVE MINUTES!
I'LL HURRY! THANK YOU SO MUCH!
He's a nice cub. I guess I can wait...
...
PHEW
...
WHAT'S UP WITH HIM? IS HE... RELIEVED?

FOR A MOMENT THERE I FORGOT... HE'S JUST A HIGH SCHOOL STUDENT...
I'M PROBABLY IN MORE PAIN THAN YOU ARE!
OUCH ...
WHAT NOW?
FSSSHHHHH
LET'S WASH... THE BLOOD OFF THE FLOOR.
...AND A CARNI-VORE...
...WHO'S USUALLY...
...VERY CONSIDERATE OF HERBIVORES.
THE TILES ARE RUINED. WHAT ARE WE GOING TO DO ABOUT THIS?
HEH HEH... WE'LL GET OUT OF HERE BEFORE THE CLEANING LADY FINDS OUT. THEN WE'LL PRETEND WE DON'T KNOW ANYTHING ABOUT IT.

TAKE MY SHIRT. YOU CAN USE IT TO STOP THE BLEEDING IF YOU WANT.
UH, NO... I'LL LEAVE THROUGH THE WINDOW AND TAKE CARE OF MY WOUNDS MYSELF.
WHY ARE YOU LIKE THIS...?
YEAH? ALL RIGHT, THEN. SEE YOU LATER.
IF YOU WERE JUST A VILLAIN, IT WOULD BE EASIER TO FAN THE FLAMES OF MY HATRED.
WHY DID YOU HAVE TO DEVOUR TEM IF YOU'RE CAPABLE OF SUCH SELF-CONTROL?
IF...
...THIS HAD HAPPENED A YEAR AGO...
...I WOULD JUST LEAVE QUIETLY...

KLNCH
I WILL NEVER...
SPURT
...FORGIVE YOU...
LOOKS LIKE WE...
...PLANTED THE SEEDS OF HATRED TODAY...

NEW YEAR'S EVE, RIZ...
DON'T EXPECT TO LIVE TO GREET THE NEW YEAR.
NEW YEAR'S EVE...? THAT'S TEN DAYS FROM NOW. OKAY.
I'LL GET READY TO DESTROY YOU.

WE'LL SETTLE THIS ONCE AND FOR ALL AS CARNIVORES IN BATTLE.

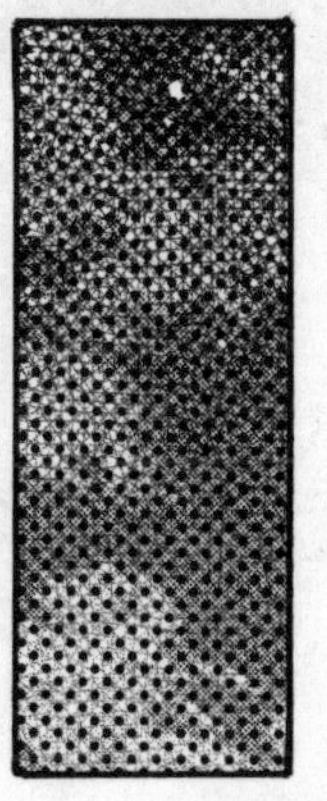

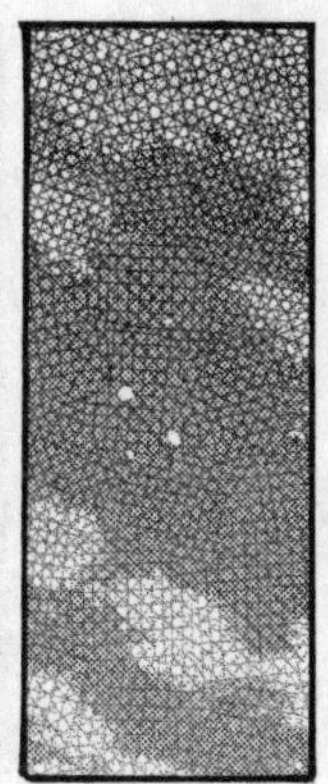

GOOD. BRING IT ON.

Legoshi went straight to Gohin's place.
YOU COULD HAVE JUST TURNED HIM IN TO THE POLICE. YOU'RE OUT OF YOUR MIND. HEH HEH...
I-I'M JUST FOLLOWING THE PRINCIPLES YOU TAUGHT ME.
I ALMOST DEVOURED AN HERBIVORE MYSELF ONCE.
SO I PREFER TO DEAL WITH RIZ PERSON-ALLY INSTEAD OF HAVING SOMEBODY ELSE PUNISH HIM.
BUT MAYBE ...
...FIGHTING THIS BATTLE IS POINTLESS AFTER ALL...
IT'S NOT LIKE IT'S GOING TO CHANGE HIM OR MAKE THE WORLD A BETTER PLACE.
DON'T COMPLI-CATE THINGS. KEEP IT SIMPLE.

GO AHEAD AND GIVE YOUR ENEMY A BEAT-DOWN.
THAT'S WHAT 17-YEAR-OLDS DO.
NOW THEN... WHAT SHOULD I TEACH YOU NEXT?
I'M GOING TO TRAIN YOU HARD STARTING TONIGHT.
GOHIN REMINDS ME A LITTLE OF MY GRANDPA...
ALL RIGHT! I'M READY TO TRAIN HARD!

Chapter 86: A Comet in the Depths

always expressionless
Female patient. As yet unidentified.
Tibetan sand foxes are considered the
nost stone-faced of carnivores. It's not that they lack
otions—they just haven't developed the facial muscles to
ess them.

LOOK AT MY PAWS. KEEP TRACKING THEM AS I MOVE THEM.
HM?
KEEP WATCHING.

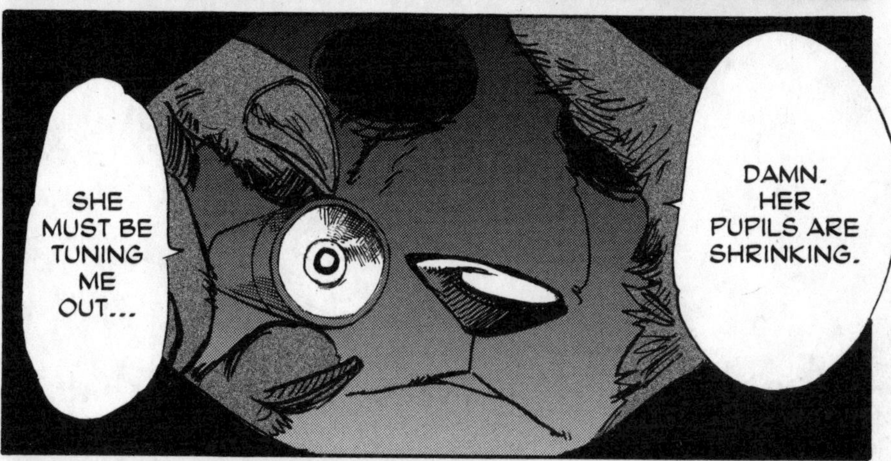
DAMN. HER PUPILS ARE SHRINKING.
SHE MUST BE TUNING ME OUT...

ARGH! AGH!
YEAH, THAT'S RIGHT... RELAX...
JUST A LITTLE LONGER...
AHHHH!

TIBETAN SAND FOX, FEMALE IN HER TWENTIES... I'M GOING TO CHECK HER VITALS NOW.
YOUR HEART RATE'S A LITTLE UNEVEN.
THIS IS THE FIRST TIME!..
...A MALE...
...
...HAS TOUCHED MY CHEST.

I THINK I KNOW... WHAT'S HAPPENING TO ME...
YAYOI. GET A ROOM READY FOR HER.
STAGE 3.
GOT IT.
DON'T WORRY, I'M A DOCTOR.
ALTHOUGH I ADMIT I AM KNOWN FOR MY DRASTIC REMEDIES, HEH HEH.... LET'S BE FRIENDS, ALL RIGHT?
Yayoi (age 41) has been a nurse at the clinic for many years.
KACHAK

GRAB
AHHHH!
TUG
OW.
LISTEN UP! I'M NOT GOING TO GO EASY ON YOU BECAUSE YOU'RE FEMALE. SO DON'T DO ANYTHING STUPID.
THIS IS A PSYCHIATRIC WARD DESIGNED TO TREAT BEASTS WHO HAVE KILLED AND DEVOURED HERBI-VORES.
OW. OWWW!

...
YOU'RE A TIBETAN SAND FOX...
THIS IS JUST WHAT I'D EXPECT FROM THE MOST STONE-FACED CARNIVORE.
DON'T WORRY, I'LL HELP YOU GET BACK IN TOUCH WITH YOUR EMOTIONS SO YOU CAN RETURN TO SOCIETY.

!
SPIT
SHE REMAINED EXPRESSIONLESS WHEN SHE SPIT ON ME.
RUB RUB
SHE'S GOING TO BE A DIFFICULT PATIENT...

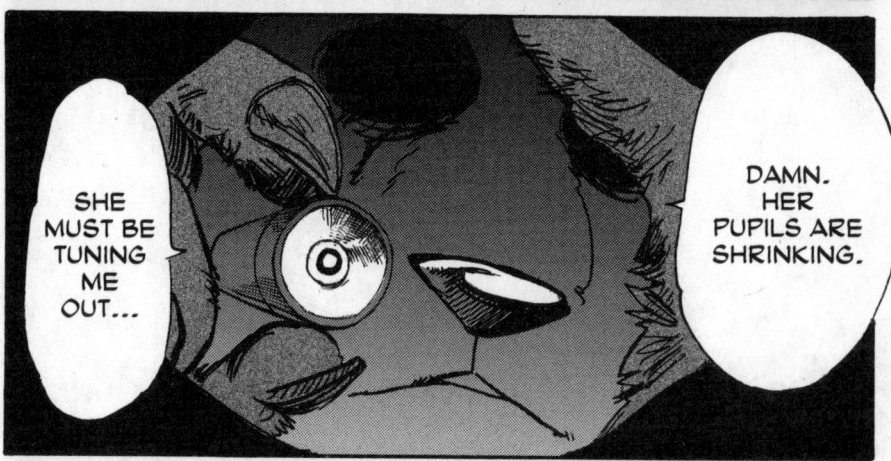

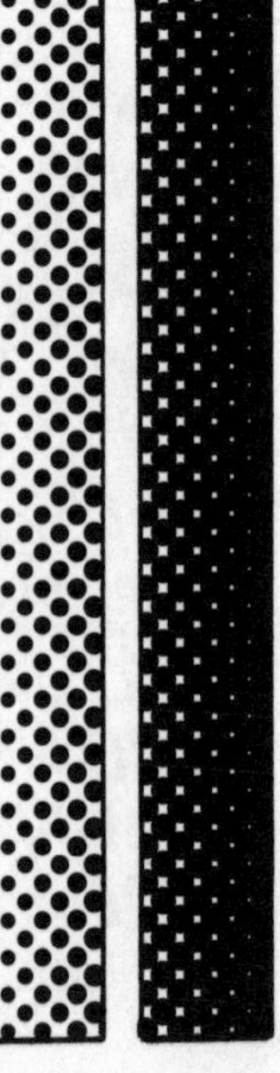

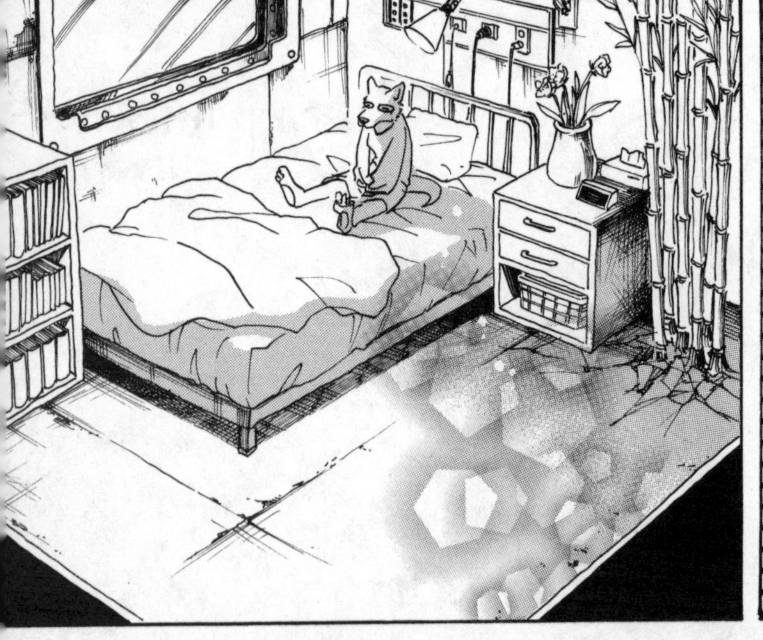

DAZED
SO I WOUND UP IN A PSYCHIATRIC HOSPITAL BECAUSE I KILLED AND DEVOURED AN HERBIVORE... WHY DID I KILL AND DEVOUR AN HERBIVORE ANYWAY...?
I AM STONE-FACED. THE DOCTOR WAS RIGHT.
I DON'T FEEL ANY-THING.
BUT FOR A TIBETAN SAND FOX...
...BEING STONE-FACED IS EASY.
MORN-ING!
SLMP
WE'LL BEGIN YOUR TREAT-MENT TODAY.

...
HA HA HA...
DO I REEK OF CIGARETTE SMOKE? I APOLOGIZE.
GO AHEAD AND HATE ME AS MUCH AS YOU WANT. THAT'S HOW MOST OF MY PATIENTS BEGIN THEIR TREATMENT.
WHEN THE MUSIC STARTS TO PLAY, I'LL ASK YOU SOME QUESTIONS. ALL YOU NEED TO DO IS ANSWER THEM.
I WON'T ASK YOU WHY YOU KILLED AND DEVOURED AN HERBIVORE UNTIL LATER. FIRST OFF, TELL ME YOUR NAME AND AGE—
GRAB
WAIT.

D-DOCTOR...
YOU CAN HAVE SEX WITH ME IF YOU WANT...

HM... IS THIS A NEW WAY OF ESCAPING REALITY?
ARE YOU THAT SCARED OF GETTING IN TOUCH WITH YOUR EMOTIONS?
IT'S NO USE TRYING TO PRETEND YOU'RE SAVAGE.
NNGH! RRGH!
SLEEPING WITH YOU WOULDN'T STOP YOU FROM BEING VIOLENT.
RRGH! RRGH! SLEEP WITH ME!
TAKE A DEEP BREATH ...
YOU'LL BE FINE. YOUR RATIONAL MIND IS JUST WITHIN REACH.
SO WHAT'S YOUR NAME?
A... UH...
HUH? COME ON... JUST BREATHE ...

I DIDN'T GET ACCEPTED TO THE COLLEGE I WANTED TO ATTEND... SO I WENT TO MY SAFETY SCHOOL.
MOST OF THE STUDENTS THERE WERE HERBIVORES. WE WERE TAUGHT THAT HERBIVORES ARE SUPERIOR TO CARNIVORES.

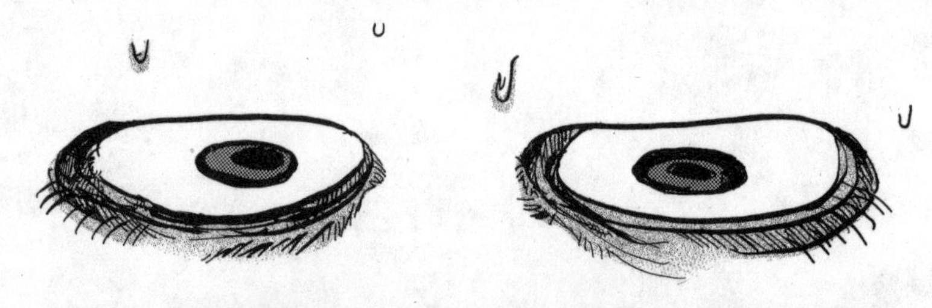

EVEN AFTER A YEAR AT SCHOOL, I DIDN'T FEEL LIKE I FIT IN.
I STARTED CUTTING CLASSES. ONE DAY I WAS WANDERING THE STREETS WHEN A HOMELESS RABBIT STARTED MESSING WITH ME...

AND...
SO... I... THAT RABBIT...

...AND THAT WAS WHERE YOU STOPPED YOUR TREATMENT.

BECAUSE I HAD FOUND THE HEART YOU'D BURIED DEEP INSIDE YOU.
I USUALLY GO WITH A MILD TREATMENT PLAN FOR PATIENTS LIKE THAT. I WASN'T SURE WHAT THE BEST COURSE WAS FOR YOU THOUGH.

BECAUSE TIBETAN SAND FOXES HIDE THEIR FEELINGS REALLY WELL.
IS TH- THAT SO?
YOU'RE NOT SHOWING ANY EMOTION NOW. DO YOU LIKE YOUR MEAL?
IT'S D- DELICIOUS. I'M ENJOYING OUR DINNER...
YEAH?
THE VEGETABLES HERE ARE VERY GOOD. IT'S THE PERFECT PLACE TO CELEBRATE YOUR DISCHARGE TONIGHT.

YOU'VE SPENT FOUR MONTHS AT THE HOSPITAL...
IT TOOK A LOT LONGER THAN I EXPECTED, BUT YOU DID VERY WELL, AI.

THAT'S BECAUSE I WAS WITH YOU FOR FOUR MONTHS...
HUH?
AT FIRST I FOUGHT YOU. THEN YOU COMFORTED ME. YOU STARTED TELLING JOKES.
I COULD TELL I WAS BEGINNING TO FEEL THINGS AGAIN.
BIG BEAR CAT

THE MORE TIME I SPENT WITH YOU...
...THE MORE MY HEART ACHED FROM THE GUILT OF KILLING AND DEVOURING THAT HERBIVORE.
THAT'S A SIGN THAT YOUR TREATMENT WAS SUCCESSFUL.
YOU'LL NEVER KILL AND DEVOUR AN HERBIVORE AGAIN.
YOU CAN RETURN TO COLLEGE NOW OR GET A JOB... LIVE THE LIFE YOU CHOOSE.
BEASTS WILL LOVE YOU NOW, EVEN IF YOU ARE STONE-FACED.
DOCTOR... I...

I'M GOING TO TURN MYSELF IN TO THE POLICE TOMOR-ROW.

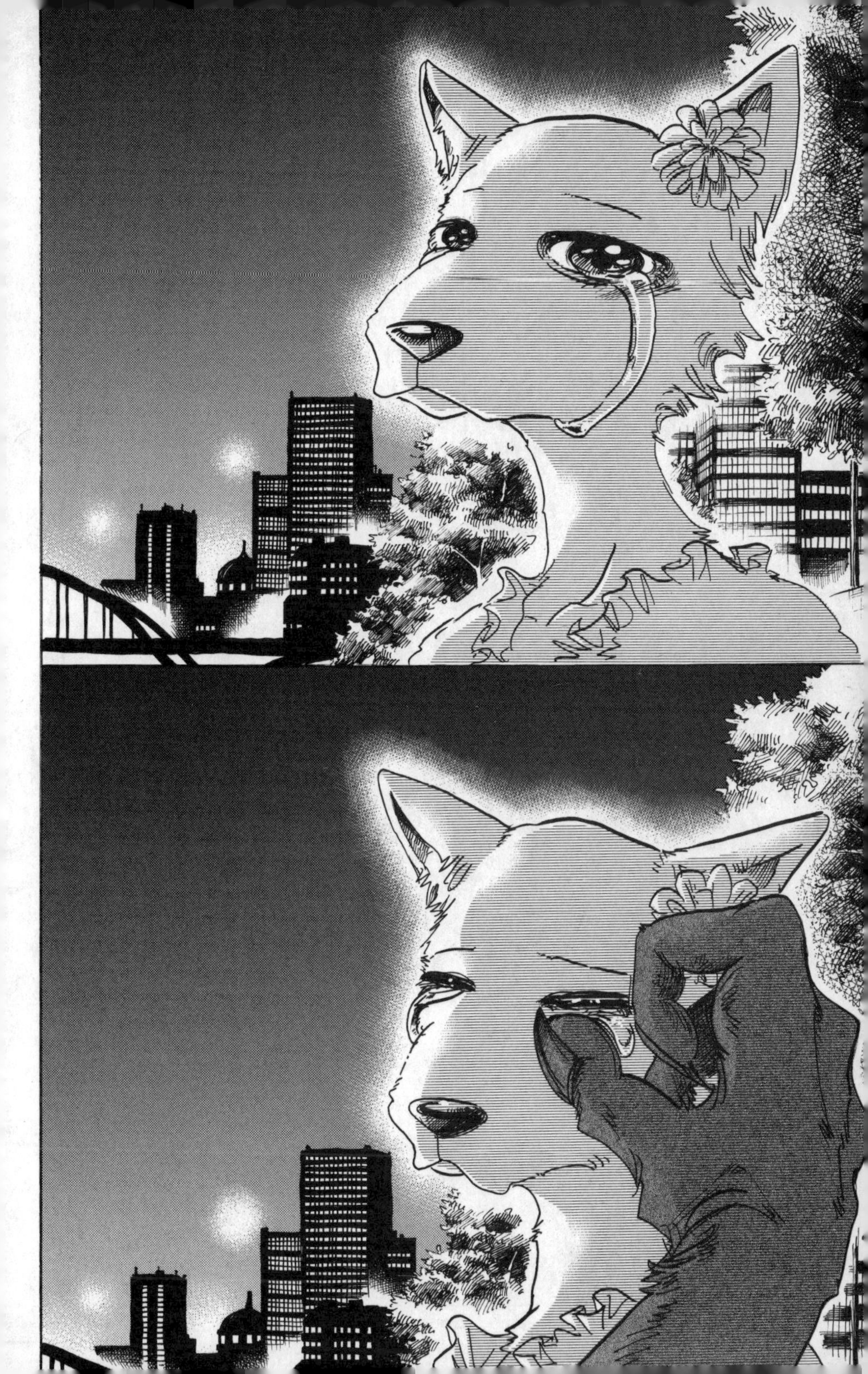

I WAS HOPING TO SEE YOU SMILE.
I WISH YOU WOULD.
YOU SAID THE BEST OUTCOME WAS FOR YOUR PATIENTS TO TURN THEM-SELVES IN TO THE AUTHORI-TIES.
THAT'S THE RIGHT THING TO DO...
BUT I CAN STILL FEEL SAD ABOUT IT... PANDAS GET EMOTIONAL.

THEN... I'LL LEAVE MY SMILE WITH YOU.
HUH?

PLEASE WAIT FOR ME... UNTIL I'M RELEASED FROM PRISON WITH A SMILE ON MY FACE.
WELL? PROMISE ME?
HMPH... IT BETTER BE A GREAT BIG BEAMING SMILE THEN.
COME BACK QUICKLY.

YOUR HORNS SMELL NICE TODAY.
I RUBBED THEM WITH HONEY-SCENTED BEESWAX TO MAKE THEM SHINE. ♡
HM... I REALLY LIKE THAT SCENT.
Chapter 87: Best Supporting Actor Award for the New Star
YOU'RE A MEMBER OF THE DRAMA CLUB, AREN'T YOU? IS IT FUN?

I HAVE A BIG PART IN THE NEW YEAR'S PERFORMANCE. WILL YOU COME SEE ME PERFORM?
OOH! OF COURSE I WILL. ♡ WHAT ROLE ARE YOU PLAYING?

A BEAUTIFUL YOUNG LAMB WHOSE SOUL IS TAKEN FROM HIM BY THE GRIM REAPER.
I DIE AT THE END.
WHAT?
YOU DIE?
YEP. I DO.

WOULD YOU FEEL SAD IF I DIED FOR REAL, RIONA?
I MIGHT CRACK UP LAUGHING.

I MEAN, WHO THE HELL IS RIONA?!
SWISH SWISH
YOU MIX UP ALL YOUR GIRL-FRIENDS' NAMES. WHO WOULD BOTHER TO ATTEND YOUR FUNERAL?

I'VE DONE IT AGAIN... AND WOW... GIRLS SURE CAN SLAY YOU WITH WORDS.
So no one would attend my funeral, huh...?
I'M IN SUCH SHOCK I STILL CAN'T RECALL HER NAME...
GOT TO PULL MYSELF TOGETHER. THINGS HAVEN'T BEEN GOING ALL THAT GREAT LATELY.
A ROLE IN WHICH I DIE A BEAUTIFUL DEATH... HOW APPROPRIATE!

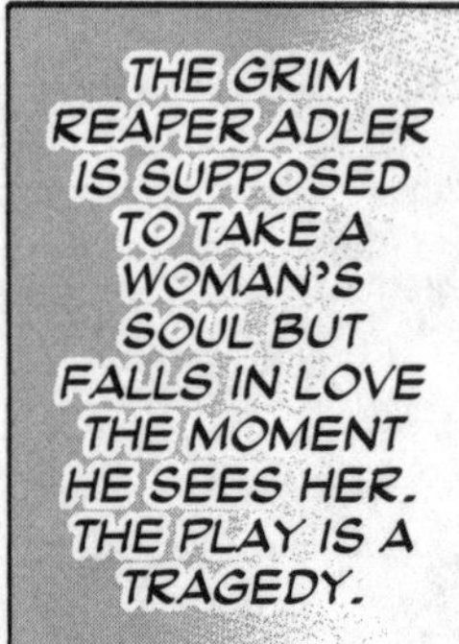

THE GRIM REAPER ADLER IS SUPPOSED TO TAKE A WOMAN'S SOUL BUT FALLS IN LOVE THE MOMENT HE SEES HER. THE PLAY IS A TRAGEDY.
THE DRAMA CLUB HAS BEEN PERFORMING ADLER FOR A LONG TIME.

THIS SHOW WILL BE A CHALLENGE. THE CASTING IS TABOO BECAUSE A CARNIVORE WILL BE TAKING AN HERBIVORE'S SOUL.

THIS UPCOMING PERFORMANCE IS UNUSUAL BECAUSE JUNO, A FEMALE WOLF, IS PLAYING THE GRIM REAPER.
AND I, A MALE SHEEP, AM PLAYING OPPOSITE HER.

JUST LIKE IN THE REAL WORLD.

A BEAUTIFUL YOUNG BOY WHOSE SOUL IS STOLEN FROM HIM... I GUESS THAT FITS...

PINA, I'M LOOKING FORWARD TO TODAY'S RUN-THROUGH.

RIZ! YOU STARTLED ME!
Aha ha ha
SO MUCH SO THAT NOW I CAN'T PEE.

SO EVEN A BEAST WHO KILLS AND DEVOURS AN HERBIVORE HAS TO TAKE A WHIZ SOMETIMES TOO, HUH? OF COURSE HE DOES...
I'M GETTING OUT OF HERE.

I'M GOING TO SETTLE THINGS WITH LEGOSHI ON NEW YEAR'S EVE.
GOOD MORN-ING.
MORNIN'! WHAT HAPPENED TO YOUR HEAD?
WHEN I SAW LEGO-SHI'S MESSED-UP FACE...
...I FIGURED SOMETHING HAPPENED BETWEEN YOU TWO. SO THAT'S HOW THINGS ARE GOING TO GO DOWN, HUH?
I wish he'd told me...
(Everyone's getting used to Legoshi looking beat-up.)

LEGOSHI AND YOU ARE THE ONLY ONES WHO KNOW I KILLED AND DEVOURED TEM.
THIS IS YOUR BUSINESS TOO.
AFTER I BEAT LEGOSHI, I'LL BE SO HYPED UP...
...I MIGHT NOT BE ABLE TO CONTROL MYSELF...
I MIGHT END UP DEVOURING YOU... STARTING WITH YOUR HEAD...
I DON'T THINK YOU SHOULD START WITH MY HEAD.
THESE HORNS WILL GET IN YOUR WAY, AND I DON'T THINK THEY'LL TASTE GOOD.

LICK
AGH...
WHAT?! NO...
SLURPP
I COULDN'T HELP MYSELF... I SMELLED HONEY ON YOUR FINGERS... SORRY.
Well... See you later at Drama Club.

ARGH!
I'VE STILL GOT ALL MY FIN-GERS...

PHEW.
...
I'M LYING ON THE BATHROOM FLOOR...
...BECAUSE MY LEGS GAVE OUT. AND NOW I FEEL RELIEVED.
I GUESS THAT MEANS...
...I WANT TO LIVE.

YES.
ALL RIGHT, EVERYONE! LET'S BEGIN OUR RUN-THROUGH! READY ON LIGHTS?
SOUND?
WE'RE READY.
PINA... YOU LOOK PALE. ARE YOU ALL RIGHT? HAVEN'T YOU MEMORIZED YOUR LINES?
HUH? I THINK SO...
PINA PROBABLY HASN'T GOTTEN ENOUGH SLEEP BECAUSE HE'S ALWAYS CHASING AFTER GIRLS.
PSST PSST PSST
HE'S REALLY HANDSOME, BUT HIS ACTING SUCKS COMPARED TO LOUIS.
SO I'M NOT ENTIRELY UNLOVABLE... THAT MAKES ME FEEL BETTER.

I'M ADLER... THE GRIM REAPER... COME TO TAKE YOUR SOUL THIS NIGHT.
IF YOU HAVE ANY LAST WORDS, MY SCYTHE WILL HEAR THEM.
...
WOULD THE GRIM REAPER BE SAT-ISFIED...
...IF I BEGGED FOR MY LIFE?

WHAT ?!
GOOD, GOOD... HE REMEM-BERS HIS LINES AT LEAST.
MY LIFE IS INDEED WORTHLESS, BUT MY LIFE IS MY OWN. MOREOVER...
THE TERROR I'LL FEEL WHEN I DIE BELONGS TO ME.
IF YOU WANT TO HEAR ME SCREAM FROM THE DEPTHS OF MY SOUL, I'LL DO SO.

NOW KILL ME!

I SHALL NOT FEAR YOU!

HUF
HUF
OOPS!
klang
SLIP

OH NO! I SPILLED PAINT ALL OVER THE PLACE! I'M SORRY!
WHAT'S WRONG WITH YOU, DOMU?!
COULD SOME FIRST-YEARS PLEASE BRING US SOME RAGS?
SORRY, GUYS! LET'S STOP REHEARSING!
...
RE-HEARSAL IS OVER!
PINA...
WHAT HAP-PENED?
HA HA... WHAT DO YOU MEAN? I'M GOING TO GET A DRINK OF WATER.
Drama Club Officers

TUP
WERE YOU WATCH-ING ME?
DID YOU SEE HOW... REAL-ISTIC HIS ACTING WAS?
HE'S GOOD-LOOKING, AND HE HAS THE SOUL OF AN ACTOR... HOW THE HELL CAN I COMPETE WITH THAT?
PHEW! I'M GLAD I CAST PINA IN THAT ROLE!
As club president, I've ful-filled my duty!

Chapter 88: An Intense Woman

BEASTARS
Vol. 10

BOSS.
A HEAD WITH HORNS... A HEAD WITH A MANE...
WHICH STUFFED HEAD IS MORE VALU-ABLE, YOU THINK?
WHAT?!

CRIMINAL ENTERPRISES LIKE OURS LOVE TO DECORATE THEIR HEAD-QUARTERS WITH TROPHIES— LIKE THE HEAD OF A RIVAL ORGANIZA-TION'S BOSS, FOR EXAMPLE...
HA HA... HOW COULD THIS TINY HEAD BE A DECO-RATIVE MEMEN-TO?
I'M NOT JOKING! IF AN ORGANIZATION THAT VIEWS US AS A THREAT WERE TO COME AFTER YOUR HEAD...
THEN YOU'D DIE IN MY PLACE, IBUKI.

TUP
WE'RE RIDING SOME GOOD WAVES. I CAN'T AFFORD TO DIE YET.
IF SOME BEASTS KILL ME, RUMORS WILL SPREAD THAT MY SUBORDINATES DID IT AND DEVOURED ME.
I DON'T WANT TO SULLY THE SHISHI-GUMI'S NAME.
OF COURSE I'D WILLINGLY DIE FOR YOU...
...BOSS.

I NEED TO GO TO THE RESTROOM... BARTENDER! TWO JACK DANIEL'S ON THE ROCKS!
I DON'T LIKE HARD LIQUOR.

WHAT?!
First time I've heard of it...
TH-THEN... HOW ABOUT A SWEET COCK-TAIL?
I'M NOT A GIRL!
HM... I'LL HAVE A PLUM WINE... WITH HOT WATER.

SO BOSS GETS DRUNK EASILY!
HE TOLD ME SOMETHING PERSONAL... HE'S BEGIN-NING TO TRUST ME!
I GUESS MY TRAGIC PAST...
...WORKED IN MY FAVOR...
ENERGY

KREEK
KLINK KLINK KLINK
EH?
KLANK
JNGL
A FEMALE CUSTOMER.

PEEK
SHE SAT DOWN RIGHT NEXT TO ME... WHAT THE HELL?

PLEASE DON'T SCREAM, LOUIS!

I HAVE MY REASONS FOR DRESSING LIKE THIS... BUT FIRST...

IT'S ME— LEGOSHI. BUT I GUESS YOU CAN TELL...
Aha ha ha
MY CROSS-DRESSING SUCKS, DOESN'T IT...?
I THOUGHT THIS WOULD BE...
...A GOOD DISGUISE, SO I COULD COME SEE YOU.
...
DO I...
...HAVE TO...
...KILL HIM TO STOP HIM FROM LOSING HIS MIND?!

THERE'S SOMETHING...
...I HAVE TO TELL YOU.
KREEK
SHFF
...
?!
A HUGE FEMALE IS HITTING ON THE BOSS!
STARE
READY TO ORDER?
HUH?!
UH... UM...
YOU'RE A WOLF, SO I RECOMMEND OUR "HOWLING BITCH" COCKTAIL.
Oh!
OKAY, I'LL HAVE THAT THEN, PLEASE...
Falsetto

ARGH! I FOUND LOUIS... BUT NOW WHAT? THE SHISHI-GUMI RETURNED SOONER THAN I EXPECTED.
HAVE TO THINK! WHAT DO I DO NOW?!
Three hours ago...
Flashback 4-Panel Theater
I WANT TO TELL LOUIS WHAT I'M GOING TO DO.
YOUR HAIR'S GROWN OUT. YOU'LL GET RECOG-NIZED.
THE SHISHI-GUMI IS PROBABLY EVEN MORE WARY THAN BEFORE.
THE ONLY DISGUISE I CAN THINK OF IS TO CROSS-DRESS...
I THINK I'VE STILL GOT SOME CLOTHES MY WIFE LEFT BEHIND WHEN SHE ABANDONED ME.
And so...
D-DO I REMIND YOU OF YOUR WIFE?
SHF
I'M GOING TO SHOOT HIM POINT-BLANK...

URK... LOUIS'S ANGER IS COMING THROUGH LOUD AND CLEAR.
I KNOW I LOOK FUNNY, BUT I HAD A SERIOUS REASON FOR COMING HERE! SO PLEASE HEAR ME OUT!

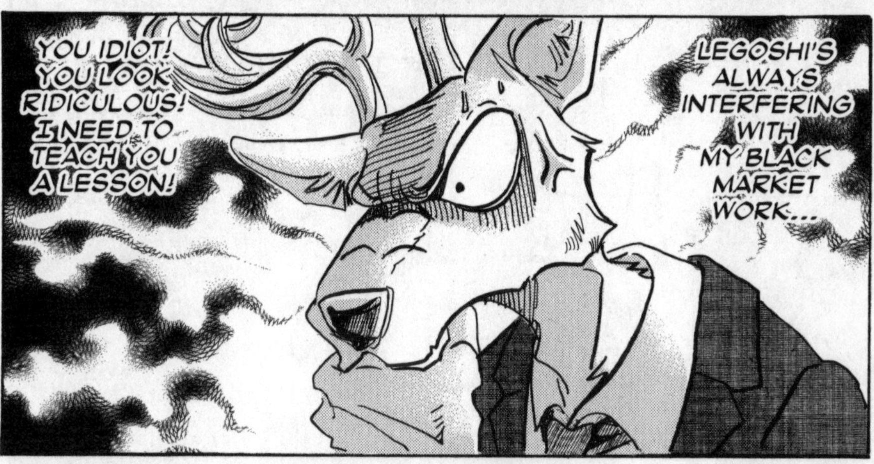
LEGOSHI'S ALWAYS INTERFERING WITH MY BLACK MARKET WORK...
YOU IDIOT! YOU LOOK RIDICULOUS! I NEED TO TEACH YOU A LESSON!

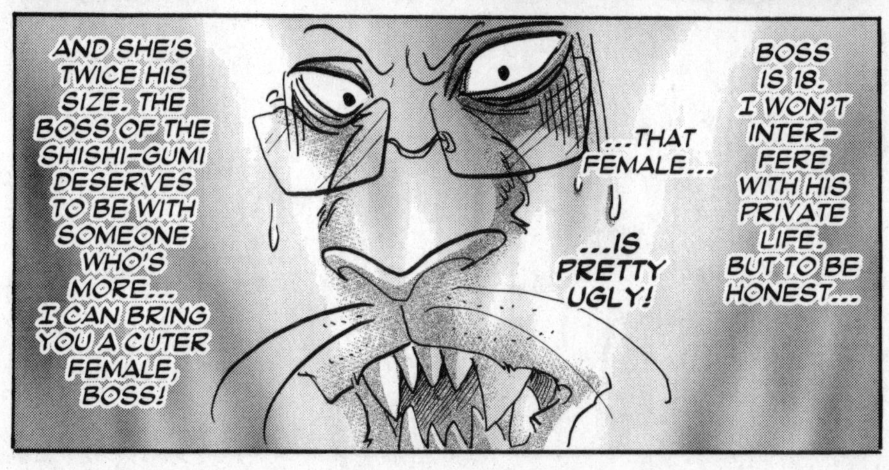
BOSS IS 18. I WON'T INTER-FERE WITH HIS PRIVATE LIFE. BUT TO BE HONEST...
...THAT FEMALE...
...IS PRETTY UGLY!
AND SHE'S TWICE HIS SIZE. THE BOSS OF THE SHISHI-GUMI DESERVES TO BE WITH SOMEONE WHO'S MORE... I CAN BRING YOU A CUTER FEMALE, BOSS!

WHAT THE HELL...
...DO WE DO ABOUT THIS?!

...
...
IBUKI!
YES-SIR!

GIVE US SOME PRIVACY.
O-OKAY!
I GUESS BOSS HAS WEIRD TASTE! WOW!

SHEESH... MY CURIOSITY WON OUT OVER...
...MY ANNOY-ANCE AND MY DUTY TO THE GANG.
CHAK
I'M CURIOUS TO HEAR WHAT MY CROSS-DRESSED JUNIOR CLASSMATE CAME TO TELL ME...
LOUIS... THANK YOU!
OH, SHUT UP...

AH... SO RIZ KILLED AND DEVOURED TEM.
THAT BROWN BEAR STAYED ON AS A STUDENT POSING AS A HARMLESS PLUSHIE...
EXACTLY! I CAN'T FORGIVE HIM FOR WHAT HE DID!
flap flap
NOW THAT YOU KNOW HE'S THE MURDERER, YOU SHOULD REPORT HIM TO THE POLICE.
HIC
WHY DOES EVERY-ONE KEEP TELLING ME THAT?! I DON'T WANT TO HAND HIM OVER TO THE POLICE!

RIZ AND I ARE BOTH CAR-NIVORES... WE'LL SEE WHO PREVAILS IN BATTLE.
IF I LOSE AND GET KILLED, THEN SO BE IT.

RIZ HURT MY HEAD THE OTHER DAY BEFORE WE STOPPED FIGHTING...
WAIT... YOU'RE PLANNING TO TAKE ON RIZ ALONE?
WE'RE DUELING ON NEW YEAR'S EVE.
LOUIS...
PLEASE COME AND BE MY WITNESS.

WHY WOULD I DO THAT?
LOUIS...
HOW MANY TIMES DO I HAVE TO TELL YOU?! I'M A BEAST OF THE BLACK MARKET NOW! I REFUSE TO GET INVOLVED WITH SCHOOL-BOY AFFAIRS ANYMORE!
GRAB
I'LL NEVER ASK YOU TO LEAVE THE BLACK MARKET AGAIN. BUT IF I'M GOING TO DIE, I WANT YOU TO BE THERE.
SO, PLEASE...!

...

...
PFFT
...

WHY ARE YOU ...?
WELL, BE-CAUSE ...
Heh heh
THE WAY YOU LOOK ...
YOU LAUGHED ...
YOU LAUGHED AT ME!
I COULDN'T HELP IT!
I'LL TAKE THAT AS A YES, THEN! WE'RE DUELING ON NEW YEAR'S EVE UNDERNEATH THE RAILWAY TRACKS AT GAZURA— IN FRONT OF THE SCHOOL. I'LL BE WAITING FOR YOU.
UHH ... HEY! I'M NOT GO-ING!
UM, BOSS?
WHERE DID THAT HUGE FEMALE GO...?
I DITCHED HER.
OH, GOOD. YOU DID THE RIGHT THING.
OF COURSE I DID.

I'M NOT GOING...
HE'S SUCH AN IDIOT.
Three days to go ...

KLTTR KLTTR
Legoshi running in high heels

UNCLE IBUKI

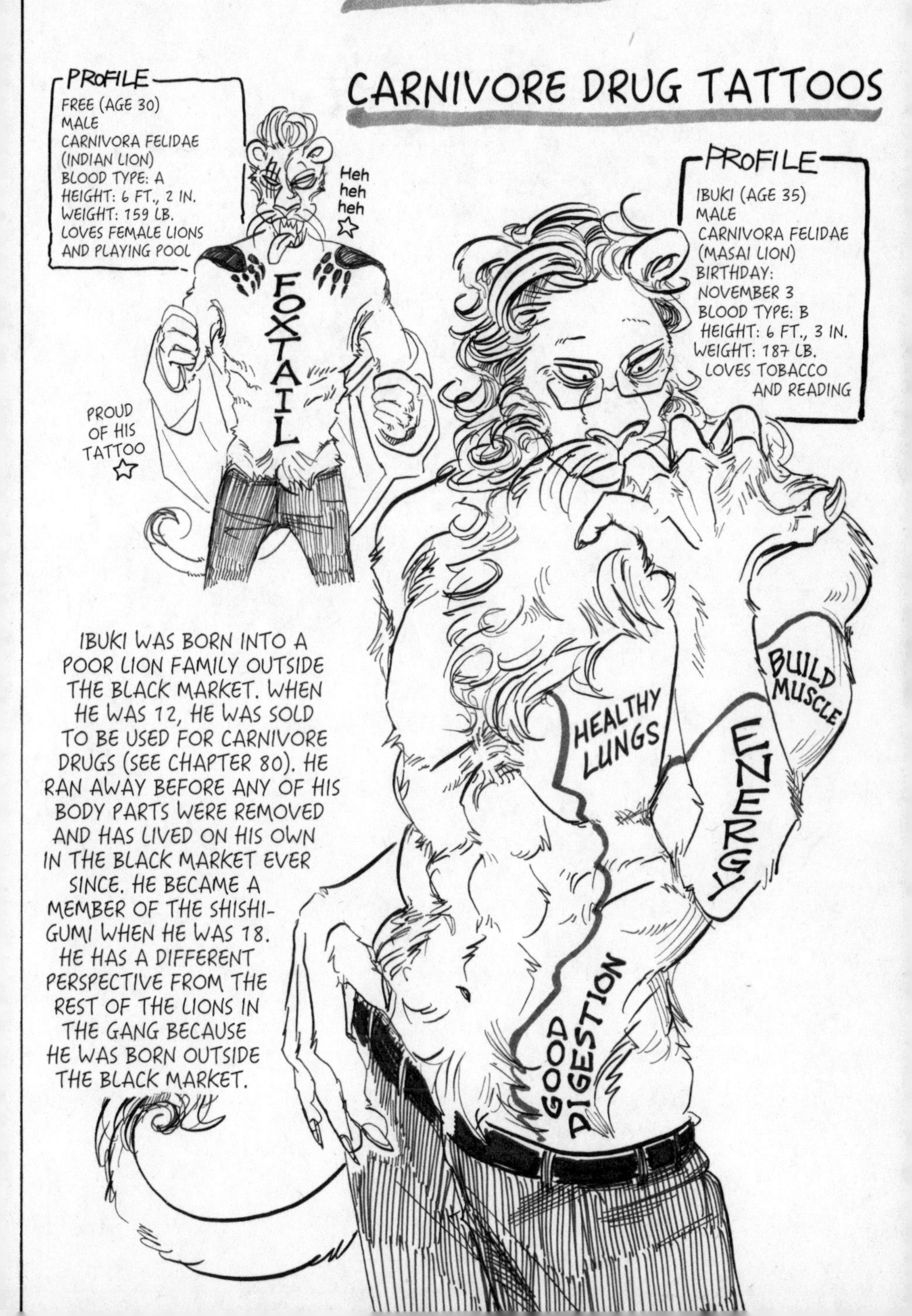

IBUKI WAS BORN INTO A POOR LION FAMILY OUTSIDE THE BLACK MARKET. WHEN HE WAS 12, HE WAS SOLD TO BE USED FOR CARNIVORE DRUGS (SEE CHAPTER 80). HE RAN AWAY BEFORE ANY OF HIS BODY PARTS WERE REMOVED AND HAS LIVED ON HIS OWN IN THE BLACK MARKET EVER SINCE. HE BECAME A MEMBER OF THE SHISHI-GUMI WHEN HE WAS 18. HE HAS A DIFFERENT PERSPECTIVE FROM THE REST OF THE LIONS IN THE GANG BECAUSE HE WAS BORN OUTSIDE THE BLACK MARKET.

A Bonus Manga Featuring Ogma, Louis's Adoptive Father.
(Behind the scenes of vol. 10)

BEASTARS Vol. 10

Paru Itagaki

What Usually Happens with BEASTARS Storyboards
(The process of developing the story)

*A BEASTARS chapter is usually 20 pages long.

This always happens.

BEASTARS Vol. 10

My short notes on each chapter

(I plan to try out a lot of different concepts for these bonus pages.)

*Apologies in advance for any omissions and errors.

Chapter 80: Picking and Choosing Smiles

- Louis tosses away his smartphone at the end. That's why I ended up titling the chapter like this.
- This is an important chapter because Louis and Ibuki grow closer.
- I enjoyed drawing the scenes about the carnivore drugs.

Chapter 81: Eyes like Two Side-by-Side Pieces of Lacquerware

- It goes without saying that the subtitle refers to Riz's eyes. (^^)
- I kept thinking that I needed to draw a scene showing Kibi and Tao together ASAP, otherwise they would remain miserable!! So I drew a lot of those scenes in the first half of this chapter.

Chapter 82: Across the Universe

- Legoshi had an experience that transcended space and time. That's how I ended up with this title.
- I finished these storyboards incredibly fast.

Chapter 83: An Ordinary Hug Handled by a Futon

- I wanted to draw Legoshi and Haru together because I hadn't done that in a while.
- I put a lot of effort into drawing the differences in their physiques—even more than before.

Chapters 84 and 85

- I thought there wouldn't be enough pages to draw everything through chapter 88, so these two chapters tell only one story.
- I made the battle scenes dynamic!!
- And simple!
- I managed to reveal some new information as well.

Chapter 86: A Comet in the Depths

- I'd been longing to draw Gohin's dream novel—a story where you insert your own names for the characters—so I'm very, very happy with this chapter. (^^)

Chapter 87: Best Supporting Actor Award for the New Star

- It takes me a long time to draw Pina, so I was exhausted the last day of drawing this chapter.
- In most of the pages, Riz is looming behind Pina...

Chapter 88: An Intense Woman

- This follows a sequence of serious chapters, so I had Legoshi show some fur for this one.
- That's really the only reason this chapter turned out this way.

THERE IS A LARGE SPACE INSIDE OF ME (ABOUT HALF THE SIZE OF A GYMNASIUM). MEMORIES AND NEW THOUGHTS AND IDEAS ARE PERFORMED IN THERE LIKE IMPROV SHOWS.

PARU ITAGAKI

Paru Itagaki began her professional career as a manga author in 2016 with the short story collection **BEAST COMPLEX**. **BEASTARS** is her first serialization. **BEASTARS** has won multiple awards in Japan, including the prestigious 2018 Manga Taisho Award.

BEASTARS

VOL. 10

VIZ Signature Edition

Story & Art by

Paru Itagaki

Translation/Tomo Kimura
English Adaptation/Annette Roman
Touch-Up Art & Lettering/Susan Daigle-Leach
Cover & Interior Design/Yukiko Whitley
Editor/Annette Roman

First published in 2018 by Akita Publishing Co., Ltd., Tokyo
English translation rights arranged with Akita Publishing Co., Ltd., through
Tuttle-Mori Agency, Inc., Tokyo

Printed in the U.S.A.

Published by VIZ Media, LLC
P.O. Box 77010
San Francisco, CA 94107

10 9 8 7 6 5 4 3 2 1
First printing, January 2021

viz.com vizsignature.com

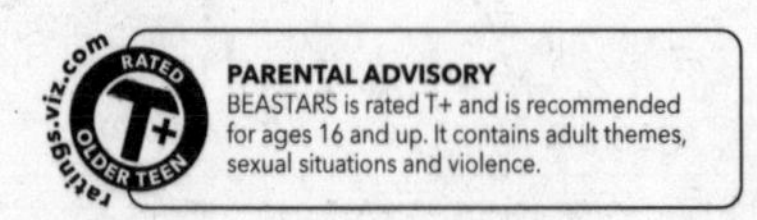

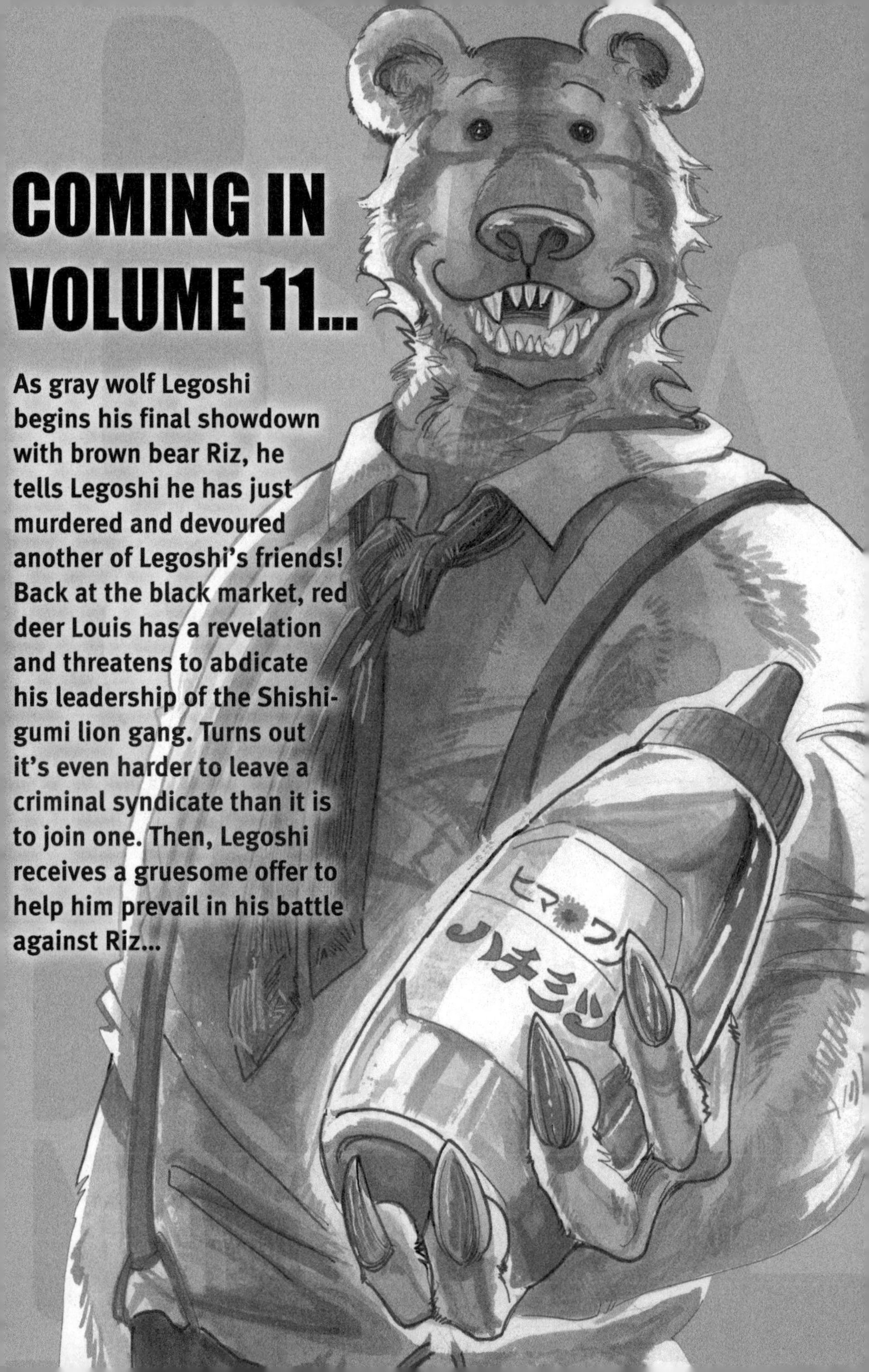
COMING IN VOLUME 11...
As gray wolf Legoshi begins his final showdown with brown bear Riz, he tells Legoshi he has just murdered and devoured another of Legoshi's friends! Back at the black market, red deer Louis has a revelation and threatens to abdicate his leadership of the Shishi-gumi lion gang. Turns out it's even harder to leave a criminal syndicate than it is to join one. Then, Legoshi receives a gruesome offer to help him prevail in his battle against Riz...

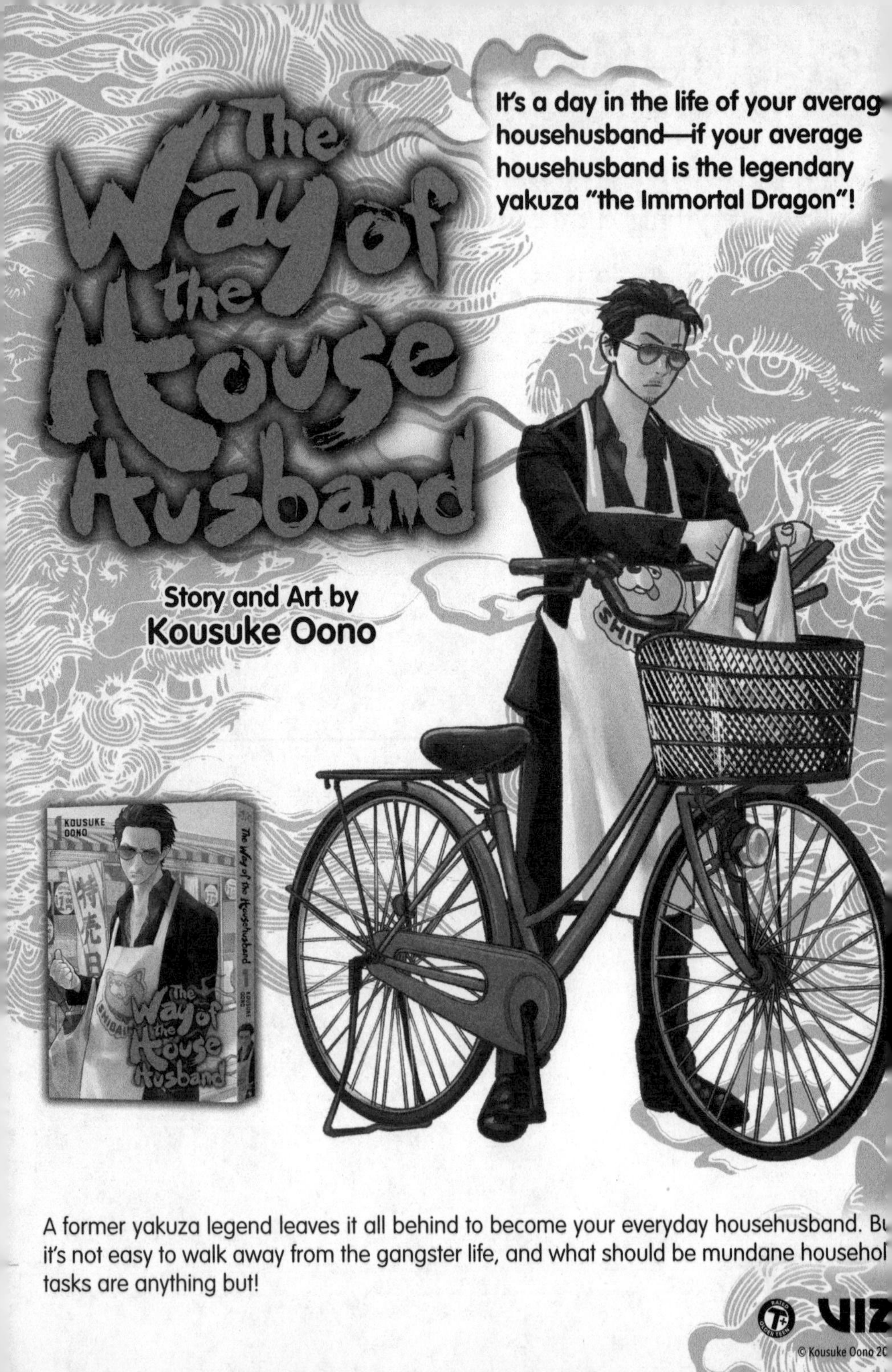
The Way of the House Husband
It's a day in the life of your averag
househusband—if your average
househusband is the legendary
yakuza "the Immortal Dragon"!
Story and Art by
Kousuke Oono
KOUSUKE OONO
The Way of the Househusband
A former yakuza legend leaves it all behind to become your everyday househusband. Bu
it's not easy to walk away from the gangster life, and what should be mundane househol
tasks are anything but!
VIZ
© Kousuke Oono 20

This is the last page.

BEASTARS reads from right to left to preserve the orientation of the original Japanese artwork.